YOUR
PERSONALITY
ASSESSMENT
BOOK

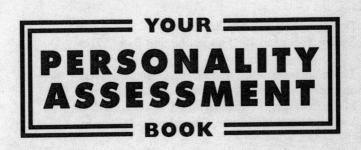

YOUR
PERSONALITY ASSESSMENT
BOOK

BEN HAMILTON

CHANCELLOR
PRESS

First published in Great Britain by
Sphere Books Ltd 1982 under the title *Book of Tests*

This edition published in 1994 by Chancellor Press
an imprint of Reed Consumer Books Ltd
Michelin House, 81 Fulham Road, London SW3 6RB
and Auckland, Melbourne, Singapore and Toronto

ISBN 1 85152 694 3

A CIP catalogue record is available from the British
Library

Printed and bound in Great Britain by Cox and Wyman Ltd

CONTENTS

ACKNOWLEDGEMENTS

All but eleven of the tests were created specially for the book by Paul James, with Dr Frank Evans, Ben Hamilton, Sarah Kendall and Ann O'Connor.

'How Suspicious Are You?' and 'Are You "In Touch"?' are by David Gunston; 'How Responsive Are You?' and 'Are You Efficient?' by Jean Black; 'How Kind Are You?' and 'Are You Stimulating To Others?' are reproduced by permission of Singer Communications, Inc, Anaheim, California, USA; 'Will You Live To Be A Hundred?' and 'Are You A Lion Or A Mouse?' by Suzanne Thomas; 'How Well Do You Know Yourself?' by Pauline Lee; 'What Are Your Secret Talents?' by Pauline Lee and 'Have You Got The Sex Factor?' by Nora Warner are reproduced by permission of Press Association Features Ltd, Fleet Street, London EC4.

1 ARE YOU A POPULAR PERSON?

The Test

Most of us like to think we are popular with our friends and that they would trust and confide in us in times of trouble, but how do we really know what people think of us?

To find out how popular you are, answer the following questions, but don't worry too much if you turn out to be low on everyone's list of popular people. In the words of Sir George Saville: 'Popularity is a crime from the moment it is sought; it is only a virtue where men have it whether they will or no.'

1   Are you a good listener and listen sympathetically to other people's troubles?
    a. Yes *b*. No

2   Do you enjoy hearing gossip?
    a. No *b*. Yes

3   Do your friends confide in you when they are worried?
    a. Always *b*. Never

4   Do you feel hurt if you offer advice and it isn't taken?
    a. No *b*. Yes

5   Do you keep your promises?
    a. Always *b*. Sometimes

6   Are you a good timekeeper and punctual for appointments?
    a. Always *b*. Sometimes

7 Do you always tell people the truth for their own benefit?
a. No *b*. Yes

8 If someone asks you to join them in anything, do you usually accept the invitation?
a. Usually, yes *b*. Not very often

9 Do you play practical jokes on your friends?
a. No *b*. Yes, all the time

10 Do you answer promptly when people write to you?
a. Yes *b*. No

11 Do you boast about your achievements and possessions?
a. No *b*. Yes

12 If someone invites you to a party or takes you out to dinner, do you write and thank them or send a 'thank-you' card?
a. Always *b*. Never

13 If someone invites you along to a party do you always take a little gift, such as chocolates or wine?
a. Yes *b*. No

14 If you give a party do you invite single people as well as couples?
a. Yes *b*. No

The Analysis

Give yourself 2 points for every question you answered with '*a*'.

24 - 28   You are obviously a nice person to know. People are important to you, you are thoughtful and want people to be happy, and this will mean that you are very popular. You don't try hard at it, but you are.

18 - 22   You are popular most of the time, but you do have one annoying habit – perhaps you are a bad time-keeper or take offence easily, which will deter people from inviting you to certain gatherings, and makes them think twice before turning to you.

10 - 16   You are well liked, but perhaps not the most popular of the bunch, and you know this. Perhaps you have one 'friend' that you don't get along with too well and may be excluded from parties to avoid embarrassing situations. Or perhaps you should be more appreciative of your friends.

8 or less   You have friends but don't make too much effort to help them because of a tinge of selfishness in your make-up. You will help them if you can, so long as you don't have to go out of your way. Just a little effort and your popularity would increase.

2 DO YOU HAVE IRRITATING HABITS ?

The Test

In any community, whether in your own family or place of work, there is going to be at least one person whom you find exasperating because of some irritating habit. You may feel your blood simmering as they push their glasses back on their nose for the umpteenth time, or pick their teeth with a matchstick. Has it, however, crossed your mind that *you* might be just as irritating to them?

Answer the following questions *truthfully*, and you may discover some irritating habits which you were unaware of.

1   Do you find yourself saying 'you know' or 'you see' or 'sort of', in every other sentence?
    a. Frequently *b*. Sometimes *c*. Never

2   Do you bite your fingernails?
    a. Yes *b*. No

3   Do you ever read at the meal table?
    a. Often *b*. Only if it is important business *c*. Never

4   Do you scratch a lot – not because you are unclean – but do you scratch your head when you think, or scratch your chest, nose or some other part of your anatomy?
    a. Frequently *b*. Sometimes *c*. Never

5   Does your partner ever tell you that you snore?
    a. Often *b*. Occasionally *c*. Never

6   Do you whistle or hum tunes to yourself, even when other people are around?
    a. All the time *b*. Sometimes *c*. Never

7   Do you sniff noisily?
    a. All the time *b*. Sometimes *c*. Not that I know of

8   Do you find that you have to do something with your hands, whether it is doodling with a pen or rolling a cigarette?

a. Frequently, it's tension *b.* Sometimes, when I'm anxious *c.* I haven't noticed

9 Do you talk about the weather a great deal?
a. Yes, often *b.* Occasionally *c.* I don't think I do

10 Do you have any little fads that you insist upon, like always putting the milk in the cup first when pouring tea, always starting the day with a glass of hot water, washing your hands frequently, or removing every bit of fat from your meat?
a. Yes *b.* No *c.* I may have

The Analysis

1. a - 10
     b - 5
	2. a - 10	3. a - 10
		     b - 5

4. a - 10
     b - 5
	5. a - 10
	     b - 5
		6. a - 10
		     b - 5

7. a - 10
     b - 5
	8. a - 10
	     b - 5
		9. a - 10
		     b - 5

10. a - 10 c - 5		

80 - 100 You are irritating and must be wearing to live with. You assume that people must accept you for what you are, but if you curbed some of your irritating habits, more people would enjoy your company.

55 - 75 You have *some* irritating habits and no doubt are told about them. At least you know what they are, but try and get a friend to caution you when you do them – you'll soon stop.

20-50   You are certainly not perfect and have one or two annoying mannerisms which just fall short of being irritating. Ask your partner what your most irritating habit is and try to stop it.

Less than 20 One of your irritating habits is probably thinking you don't have any. Get someone who knows you well to check your answers. If they are right – well done!

3   HOW SELF-CONFIDENT ARE YOU ?

The Test

> 'They can do all because they think they can.'
> VIRGIL 'Aeneid'

If you believe in yourself then others will believe in you too. It's easy to say 'have confidence in yourself', but not so easy to achieve. Some are born with it, others not, and to those who haven't got it, or have lost it, it takes a long time to build up.

To discover how confident you are, answer the following questions – confidently.

1   Does using the telephone worry you?
a. Yes
b. Only if I have to speak to someone I don't know
c. No, it doesn't worry me

2   Are you afraid of making a complaint if something you have bought is faulty?
a. I keep quiet about it

b. I'll write a letter of complaint, not a personal one

c. I don't mind making a scene, as long as I have my rights

3   If you were travelling by bus but only had a £5 note, would you:

    a. Walk home so as not to cause a fuss?

    b. Buy something you didn't really want to get some change?

    c. Get on the bus and put up with any moans from the conductor?

4   You once knocked over a vase in a shop and broke it and were made to pay for it. Did you:

    a. Avoid the shop altogether?

    b. Only go in when the manager was not around

    c. Go in as if nothing had happened

5   You arrive at a party wearing the same outfit as someone else. Do you: (*women only*)

    a. Sneak out and change?

    b. Avoid the woman and apologise if you meet her?

    c. Go up and compliment her on her good taste?

6   You want to buy some sexy underwear as a present for your partner. Do you:

    a. Send for it by post?

    b. Go to a shop in the next town where no-one knows you?

    c. Go to a local shop, not caring what anyone thinks?

7   You desperately want a day off work to go to the sales or a football match. Do you:

    a. Not go because you daren't ask for time off?

    b. Ring up and say you are ill?

    c. Go to work and pretend to be ill, leaving early?

8   You are at a small dinner party with a host and hostess whom you don't know, and suddenly in the middle of dinner, find yourself desperately wanting to spend a penny. Do you:
    a. Ask where the lavatory is?
    b. Say you have something stuck in a tooth and it is aching and retreat to the bathroom?
    c. Hold it, and wait until after the meal?

9   Your guests compliment you on your excellent dessert, which actually came out of a packet. Do you:
    a. Thank them, telling them it is your speciality?
    b. Smile graciously, blush and feel embarrassed about it?
    c. Tell them it came out of a packet?

10 Your neighbour's dog digs up your best rose tree. Do you:
    a. Storm round to the neighbour demanding that the dog be put down?
    b. Put the tree back and say nothing?
    c. Thump the dog, glare at it each time it looks at you, but say nothing to the neighbour?

The Analysis

1.	c - 3	2.	c - 3	3.	c - 3
	b - 1		b - 1		b - 1
4.	c - 3	5.	c - 3	6.	c - 3
					b - 1
7.	c - 3	8.	a - 3	9.	a - 3
			b - 1		c - 1
10.	a - 3
	c - 1

24 - 30   You have lots of self-confidence and don't mind telling the little white lie to get you out of a spot. You are prepared to stand up for your rights and will go to any lengths to see that justice is done.

15 - 23   Basically you are a confident person, but sometimes you have a guilty conscience, and probably blush too. Often you fail where you could succeed because your nerve lets you down at the last minute.

14 or less   You have little self-confidence and wouldn't say 'boo' to a goose in case it said 'boo' back. You will put up with any situation to keep the peace and avoid a scene.

4   HOW PATIENT ARE YOU ?

The Test

Patience may be a virtue, but it is not an easy virtue if you haven't got it. Perhaps you pray 'Dear Lord, give me patience – but hurry'. Nowadays, patience is important to enable us to cope with the pressures of work, or unemployment, relationships, rail strikes and red tape.

   To discover if patience is one of your virtues, answer the questions below:

1   If you have to make a telephone call and the line is continually engaged, do you:
    a. Keep on until it is free?
    b. Slam the phone down in disgust and give up?

2   If someone disagrees with you, do you:
    a. Calmly tell them your point of view and keep quiet?
    b. Argue it out until they see your point of view?

3   If you are unable to find something that you want, do you:
    a. Keep searching until you find it?
    b. Give up looking?

4   Have you ever slammed the telephone receiver down on anyone?
    a. No *b*. Yes

5   Have you ever walked out of a room and slammed the door?
    a. No *b*. Yes

6   Do you get upset if things don't go your way?
    a. No *b*. Yes

7   Do the questions that children ask continually irritate you?
    a. Never *b*. Frequently

8   If you were in the middle of watching something on TV and a child wanted you to read him a story, would you:
    a. Switch off and read the story?
    b. Say it would have to wait until the programme was over?

9   If your dog began barking because he wanted a walk, would you:
    a. Go and soothe it and take it out?
    b. Shout at it until it shut up?

10 If you dash off to the shop and arrive just as the 'closed' sign appears on the door, do you:
    a. Go home and come back another day?
    b. Stand outside stamping your foot on the pavement and shaking your fist at the assistant?

11 You make yourself a pullover and when you try it on it is much too big. Do you:
    a. Undo it and start again?
    b. Throw it down in disgust and never wear it?

12 You are waiting for the 10.30 am train. When at 10.45 there is still no sign of the train, do you:
    a. Think it has been delayed and will be along in a minute?
    b. Stomp along the platform and demand from the station master what has happened to the train?

The Analysis

Give yourself 10 points for each '*a*' answer.

100 - 120   You have the patience of Job. It takes a lot to ruffle you and you take everything in your stride. You remain calm in a crisis and have endless patience over any task you set yourself, and are especially patient with children.

60 - 90   You can be patient when you want to be, but there are times when people annoy you and you get very impatient with them. You get frustrated with others if they don't behave as you expect them to. If you are doing something that you enjoy and will benefit from, you have unending patience.

50 or less Your nerves frequently get frayed and it doesn't take too much to make your patience snap. Sometimes you don't stay as calm as you should and get needlessly upset. Try counting to ten next time.

5 HOW SUSPICIOUS ARE YOU ?

The Test

One of the worst habits we can develop is that of imputing bad motives to others. Of course we have to be reasonably guarded, especially with strangers. But we should be prepared to give others the benefit of the doubt by assuming they mean well until we prove the contrary.

Answer yes or no to the following questions:

1 Are you prone to think that people dislike you?

2 Do you think that family and friends talk about you among themselves?

3 Do you take a long time getting to know people?

4 Do you have to know them a long time before you trust them?

5 People are being especially kind and attentive. Are you wondering what they want?

6 Are you slow to forget an injury?

7 Do you believe that every man has his price?

8   Do you believe that most people behave themselves only because they are afraid of being caught?

9   Do you believe that most married couples would be unfaithful if they had the opportunity and thought they could get away with it?

10   The only way you can be sure that people are doing their work properly is to supervise them all the time. Do you think this is true?

11   Would you never employ anyone unless he or she were recommended by someone you knew?

12   You are on your way to catch a bus. A local carpenter and his mate arrive to do a job for you. Would you put off going out rather than leave them alone in the house?

13   Something that belongs to you is not in its usual place. Is your first reaction 'Someone has taken it', rather than that it must have been mislaid?

14   You are snuggled down in bed. Suddenly you start wondering whether you locked all the doors. Would you get up and check?

15   Do you dislike lending anything?

16   Have you ever weighed a packed product?

17   You need to ask the way in a strange city. A police officer is nowhere in sight. Would you ask more than one person?

18 A friend makes an excuse to cancel an appointment. Would you think that, really, it was because he/she did not want to come?

19 Do you carry any kind of lucky charm?

20 Do you think to yourself, 'I'm not really surprised', when a friend lets you down?

The Analysis

Count 5 points for every NO.

70 + You are much too gullible, and too afraid of giving offence.

60 - 70 You have a well-balanced outlook and are not over-suspicious, but keep a sensible caution in your personality.

Less You must be a very uncomfortable person to live with.

6 HOW DOMINANT ARE YOU ?

The Test

Both men and women can take on a dominant role in life. Some need to be dominated and others love to dominate.
  This test will tell you on which side of the fence you are likely to fall.

1 Do you find officials, bureaucrats and red tape difficult to tolerate?

2   Do you make the major decisions in your household?

3   Do certain attitudes on television make you very angry sometimes, so that your blood boils?

4   Do you keep on with an argument until you think you have won?

5   If you are in your car and see another driver do something stupid, do you feel like hitting him?

6   Do you make rude signs at other drivers?

7   Would you demand an explanation if you saw a traffic warden writing a ticket for your car?

8   Do you get impatient if somebody cannot follow what you consider to be a simple explanation?

9   Are you intolerant with people who don't understand your tastes?

10 If your partner bought something you didn't like, would you ask them to take it back?

11 If you bought something for your partner and he/she didn't like it, would you feel let down?

12 If you feel a workman has done a bad job, do you storm round and demand compensation?

13 Do you enjoy a position of authority?

14 Do you ever deliberately make others feel small?

15 Do you swear a lot?

16 Do you find politicians unbearable?

17 Do you feel justified in speaking your mind, regardless of the consequences?

18 If you objected to the way another person behaved would you tell them so?

19 Do you ever thump your fists on the table during an argument?

20 If you find some slight fault with a meal in a restaurant do you insist on seeing the manager?

The Analysis

Affirmative answers will show dominance, so award yourself 10 points for every question you answered with YES.

150 - 200 You are dominant to the point of being aggressive and must be difficult to live with. Some circumstance beyond your control may have resulted in your desire to dominate – they do say if Napoleon had been a few inches taller, the history of Europe would have been quite different! Take care you do not get compared with Hitler.

70 - 140 You have a tough exterior which leads people to believe that you are always unyielding. Occasionally the mask slips to reveal an old softy underneath, but you are not afraid to speak your mind and demand your rights.

20 - 60 It takes a lot to get you angry and you prefer to be dominated than to dominate. If, however, you feel that you have been treated unfairly, you are quite capable of holding your own and can surprise people with a sudden outburst.

10 or less You are submissive and need to be dominated. You don't stand up for yourself and allow people to walk all over you – especially those you love. Try and be stronger – if you didn't behave like a doormat, people wouldn't tread on you.

7 HOW KIND ARE YOU ?

The Test

Kind people are always welcome and well liked. The reason why there are not as many kind people as there might be is that being kind means putting others first. This often requires effort, time and trouble, which many of us prefer to use selfishly.

Try this test to see whether you are a kind person. Answer yes or no to each question.

1 Are you sufficiently interested and concerned to enquire about other people?

2 Do you remember names and faces and associate them successfully?

3 Do you remember the bits of news people tell you about themselves and their families?

4 Do you make a note of birthdays and special days so that you remember in time?

17

5   Are you quick to show appreciation, offer sympathy, praise, and congratulate?

6   Do you enjoy amusing children and looking after pets?

7   Would you go out of your way to help a stranger?

8   Are you quick to offer hospitality?

9   Would you try to ensure that everybody felt comfortable and nobody felt out of it?

10 Do you do your fair share of the cleaning up and the domestic chores generally?

11 Does it hurt you to see someone in trouble, unhappy, lonely?

12 Would you do something about it if you could?

13 If this meant putting yourself to trouble and inconvenience, such as missing an appointment or shouldering a responsibility, would you still do something?

14 Are you there when the family and your friends need active or moral support?

15 Are you quick to offer to do things without being asked?

16 Are you kind to everybody, not just to those you wish to impress?

17 Can people rely on you to keep your word and your promises?

18   Can your friends trust you not to discuss them with other people?

19   Are you quick to fit in when people want to change the subject, be quiet, be left entirely alone, or, conversely, when they want company?

20   Are you slow to impute bad motives as well as being quick to forgive and forget?

The Analysis

Score 5 points for every YES.

60 - 100   You can count yourself a kind person because you care about other people and their feelings. You have enough imagination and sensitivity to put yourself in their shoes and are not only ready to help, but also to make allowances.

Less   No, you are not a kind person. There's no need to say any more.

8   ARE YOU 'IN TOUCH' ?

The Test

Are you really 'in touch' with other people – linked to them by the heartwarming medium of contact itself? For the touch – loving, kind, meaningful, warm, humane – is a very special way of expressing affection or friendliness, understanding or sympathy that may go far deeper than words.
    See how you compare in this type of communication:

1 In ordinary life, do you hold hands with any adult?
a. Often *b*. Sometimes *c*. Never

2 Do you get down on the floor and romp with your (or any) young children?
a. Often *b*. Sometimes *c*. Never

3 Do you generally shake hands with older relatives or friends?
a. Often *b*. Sometimes *c*. Never

4 When helping someone on with a coat, do you finish the process with a light, friendly pat or pressure on the arms or shoulders?
a. Often *b*. Sometimes *c*. Never

5 As a rule, are you the sort of person who would lightly ruffle a youngster's hair as a gesture of affection, pride or joy?
a. Often *b*. Sometimes *c*. Never

6 Are you yourself the recipient of the single but meaningful touch that invariably evokes an atmosphere of love or devotion?
a. Often *b*. Sometimes *c*. Never

7 Is it likely to sadden you if another person says: 'Don't touch me!'?
a. Often *b*. Sometimes *c*. Never

8 When approaching a sick person, is your instinct to grasp one or both of their hands in your own, whether or not you actually do so?
a. Often *b*. Sometimes *c*. Never

9 Do you yourself react favourably to a squeeze of the arm?
a. Often *b*. Sometimes *c*. Never

10 Are you the sort of person another can readily put an arm around?
    a. Often *b*. Sometimes *c*. Never

11 Do you enjoy the sort of party games where everyone is expected to link hands or arms?
    a. Often *b*. Sometimes *c*. Never

12 Do young children (or animals) readily climb onto your lap?
    a. Often *b*. Sometimes *c*. Never

13 Have you a warm, firm, friendly, but not oppressive handshake?
    a. Often *b*. Sometimes *c*. Never

14 In conversation, do you lightly pat your listener's wrist or arm to emphasise a significant or amusing point?
    a. Often *b*. Sometimes *c*. Never

15 On the occasions when you feel like it, do you actually put a protective arm around someone – a child or an adult – instead of stifling the instinct?
    a. Often *b*. Sometimes *c*. Never

16 Do you ever envy the freedom and simplicity with which Latin people embrace each other?
    a. Often *b*. Sometimes *c*. Never

17 There are, of course, kisses and kisses, but when you kiss someone, whatever the person's age, do you mean it?
    a. Often *b*. Sometimes *c*. Never

18 Do you think it is beneficial to literally give someone a pat on the back?
    a. Often *b*. Sometimes *c*. Never

19 Are your own hands expressive in touching others?
    a. Often *b*. Sometimes *c*. Never

20 On the whole, do you think people regret missing
    opportunities for being 'in touch' when they might so
    easily have been?
    a. Often *b*. Sometimes *c*. Never

The Analysis

For every OFTEN give yourself 10 points
For every SOMETIMES give yourself 5 points
For every NEVER give yourself 1 point

150 +   You are clearly aware of the language of touch,
            and need no advice from us.

100 - 150 You are a borderline case, and hesitate to be
            really 'in touch'. Why not let your instincts rule
            you for a change? The chances of a rebuff are
            much slighter than you think.

Less   It is not much good feeling kindness, love, sym-
            pathy and friendliness unless you can show it.
            You probably feel some or all of these, but hold
            back from any physical demonstration. 'Touch
            has its own magic. It can express love and ease
            pain, and can give mankind its humanity.'

9 HOW VAIN ARE YOU ?

The Test

Most of us have a certain amount of vanity, pride in our appearance, would hate to think our looks were discussed behind our backs, and would die rather than have people hint that we have b.o. Some people, however, can take vanity too far. How close are you to becoming a peacock? The following test will tell you.

1 Whenever you pass a shop window do you look at your reflection in the glass?
   a. Always b. Sometimes c. Never

2 Do you brush or comb your hair before anybody – even members of your family – see you in the morning?
   a. Every day b. Only on working days c. Never

3 If you had just washed your hair and it was still wet when someone called would you:
   a. Hide and not answer the door?
   b. Shout from the bathroom that you are having a shower and quickly dry your hair before you appear?
   c. Answer the door immediately and apologise for your wet hair?

4 Do you use deodorants and body lotions?
   a. All the time b. Only on special occasions c. Never

5 When dining in a restaurant do you sit:
   a. With your back to everyone else in the restaurant?
   b. Facing everyone so that you can be seen?
   c. Anywhere?

6 Do you use beauty aids, such as wigs, make-up, false eyelashes, or padded bras?
   a. Every day without fail
   b. Only on social occasions
   c. Never

7 Have you ever contemplated cosmetic surgery of any kind?
   a. Each time you look in a mirror
   b. Only when you really think about it
   c. Couldn't care less about your hooked nose or saggy eyes

8 Do you look at photographs of yourself and:
   a. Feel surprised at how good you look?
   b. Think you look perfectly stunning?
   c. Cringe in horror?

9 Do you file and polish your nails?
   a. Frequently b. Occasionally c. Never

10 In the summer do you attempt to get a sun tan?
   a. Every time the sun peeps out
   b. Only in a spare moment if the sun happens to be shining
   c. Never think about it

The Analysis

1.		2.		3.		4.	
a - 3		a - 3		a - 3		a - 3	
b - 2		b - 2		b - 2		b - 2	
c - 1		c - 1		c - 1		c - 1	

5.		6.		7.		8.	
a - 2		a - 3		a - 3		a - 2	
b - 3		b - 2		b - 2		b - 3	
c - 1		c - 1		c - 1		c - 1	

24

9. a - 3   10. a - 3
   b - 2   b - 2
   c - 1   c - 1

20 - 30 You are incredibly vain, enjoying the attention of others, and like to be the centre of attraction. You will go out of your way to create an image and don't mind stealing the limelight.

15 - 19 You take pride in your appearance but you want people to accept you for what you are rather than how you look. You are prepared to make an extra special effort occasionally in the hope of being noticed.

10 - 15 You couldn't care less about what people think about you and are inclined to slovenliness. Perhaps you should take a little more care with the way you look.

10 ARE YOU A PESSIMIST OR AN OPTIMIST ?

The Test

'The optimist proclaims that we live in the best of all possible worlds; and the pessimist fears this is true.'

JAMES BRANCH CABELL (1926)

Our outlook on life can be greatly coloured, depending on whether we look at it through rose-coloured glasses, or glare at it through the gloom.

The following questions are designed to show how you are looking at the world:

1   Do you always feel enthusiastic about a new project or venture?
    a. Yes *b*. No

2   Do you expect things you undertake to be criticised?
    a. Yes *b*. No

3   If you are planning a barbeque do you feel certain it will rain?
    a. Yes *b*. No

4   If someone agrees with you or compliments you, do you suspect their motives?
    a. Yes *b*. No

5   Do you often feel depressed?
    a. Yes *b*. No

6   Do you find it difficult to get to sleep at night because your mind is too active?
    a. Yes *b*. No

7   Do you hesitate to trust someone who has let you down in the past?
    a. Yes *b*. No

8   Do you ever feel that people misunderstand you?
    a. Yes *b*. No

9   Do you agree to proposals readily or do you have to consider the consequences first?
    a. I think carefully first
    b. I say yes straight away

10   If you employed a babysitter (or dogsitter) would you make sure all valuables were locked away before leaving the house?
     a. Yes *b.* No

11   Do you ever refuse a challenge because you know it will be a disaster from the start?
     a. Yes *b.* No

12   Do you lend things to friends, confident that you will get them back?
     a. Yes *b.* No

The Analysis

Give yourself 10 points for each of the following answers:

1. a	2. b	3. b	4. b
5. b	6. b	7. b	8. b
9. b	10. b	11. b	12. a

100 - 120   The eternal optimist, you no doubt expected to get a high score. You are a confident person and have few doubts about success. You are very positive and if knocked down soon get back on your feet again. You may have a tendency to be *too* optimistic and too trusting, which could lead you into trouble.

50 - 90   You have a sensible attitude to life, and are naturally cautious without being pessimistic. You believe that prevention is better than cure.

40 or less   Oh, you pessimist! Constantly looking on the black side. Doomed to failure because that's what you always expect. Try and brighten up a little.

11 ARE YOU ABSENTMINDED ?

The Test

To be absentminded, one doesn't have to be the proverbial 'professor' or an eccentric old lady. All of us are vague sometimes, but some more so than others.

Women should be particularly honest in answering the following questions. Dorothy Parker once said that 'women and elephants never forget', but you may be the exception to the rule.

1 Do you ever call somebody by the wrong name?
   a. Occasionally *b*. Frequently *c*. Never

2 Have you ever put your own doorkey in someone else's lock unintentionally?
   a. Once or twice *b*. All the time *c*. Never

3 Do you ever look round the carpark for the car you owned prior to your present one?
   a. Only when I first changed cars
   b. Quite often
   c. Never

4 When making a phone call, have you ever dialled the number of someone else you know by mistake?
   a. Once or twice *b*. Often *c*. Never

5 Have you ever left a function wearing someone else's hat or coat?
   a. Once *b*. Often *c*. Never

6 Have you ever put on odd shoes?
   a. Once *b*. More than once *c*. Never

7 Are you in the habit of leaving things behind?
   a. Yes *b*. A couple of times *c*. Never

8 Have you ever written your signature
   using your maiden name by mistake?
   (*women only*)
   a. Yes, many times
   b. Only once or twice
   c. Never

9 Have you ever addressed a colleague at work by your
   wife's or girlfriend's name? (*men only*)
   a. Once *b*. Often *c*. Never

10 Have you ever turned up for an appointment a day or
   a week early?
   a. Once *b*. More than once *c*. Never

11 Do you ever forget appointments altogether?
   a. Frequently *b*. Occasionally *c*. Never

12 Have you ever forgotten your partner's birthday?
   a. Often *b*. Once *c*. Never

13 Do you ever mislay things of value?
   a. Often *b*. Occasionally *c*. Never

14 Have you ever taken something to the cleaners and
   forgotten to collect it?
   a. Once *b*. More than once *c*. Never

The Analysis

For each question that you answer with 'C' give yourself
10 points. 130 is the highest score you can obtain.

100 - 130	You are a very reliable person, completely in control, and can be depended upon to keep things in mind. Well done!
50 - 90	Your mind is frequently preoccupied and you are apt to be absentminded. You probably have to write down everything important. Your memory is quite good but things can be overlooked.
20 - 40	Your absentmindedness is caused by inattentiveness – milk boils over, puddings boil dry, dental appointments are missed. Try and pay more attention.
0 - 10	You're on the pathway to eccentricity if you don't watch out!

12 WILL YOU ACCEPT A CHALLENGE ?

The Test

You must have heard children when playing challenge their playmates, 'I bet you daren't . . . ' to which the answer invariably is, 'I bet I dare!'

Adults also find it difficult to resist a challenge, although we have more awareness of the dangers inherent in some cases.

Do you find an element of danger stimulating and are you a daring person? Let's find out . . .

1 If you saw a cat stuck half-way up a tree would you:
   a. Climb up and get it down?
   b. Call the fire brigade?
   c. Leave it there to get down on its own?

2 If a friend dared you to 'streak', would you:
   a. Rip your clothes off at once?
   b. Agree to do it when no-one was about?
   c. Flatly refuse?

3 Would you ever consider giving up a secure job to become an actor, artist or writer?
   a. Yes
   b. Only if I could go back to my job if I failed
   c. Certainly not

4 If you had the chance to cross the Channel in a hot-air balloon, would you take it?
   a. Yes *b.* Only if I knew it was safe *c.* No way

5 Would you take up parachuting as a hobby if you could do so?
   a. Yes
   b. Only after a long period of training
   c. Never

6 Do you ever gamble on horses, even if only on the classic races?
   a. Yes
   b. Only if the horse is a dead cert
   c. I wouldn't waste my money

7 Would you go for a midnight swim – in January?
   a. Yes *b.* Only in a hot country *c.* Never

8 If you could disguise your appearance, would you have the nerve to make an appointment with your boss and tell him exactly what you thought of him?
a. I'd love the chance
b. Only if I could be sure I wouldn't lose my job
c. Certainly not

9 Would you spend the night in a house that was reputedly haunted?
a. Yes
b. Only if somebody else was with me
c. No.

10 Do you leave home at the last minute and risk being late for appointments?
a. Yes *b.* Occasionally *c.* No, I always leave early

11 If a fortune-teller warned you not to do something, would you still go ahead and do it?
a. Of course *b.* It depends on what it was *c.* No

12 Do you enjoy taking risks?
a. Yes *b.* Only if I'm sure there is no danger *c.* No

The Analysis

Give yourself 5 points for each 'a' answer; 2 points for each 'b' answer, and 0 points for each 'c' answer.

50 - 60 You are very daring indeed, prepared to walk where angels fear to tread, and hang the consequences. Although your risks often pay off, you can come unstuck as at times you can be foolhardy.

25 - 48 You find an element of risk stimulating, but at the same time you exercise a sensible caution, sometimes you get very enthusiastic about an idea but your nerve fails you at the last moment.

24 or less You have no ambitions to be Superman and are only prepared to take 'risks' if there is no risk. Occasionally you will do something madly daring, but you feel afraid to undertake simple no-risk tasks sometimes.

13   DO YOU HAVE A JEALOUS STREAK ?

The Test

Jealousy is born out of many things – a feeling of rejection, deprivation, or unrequited love.

An old German proverb says, 'Where there is no jealousy there is no love', yet Ovid claimed that a love that is fed by jealousy dies hard. Whatever the cause, it can be a painful condition.

Most of us have felt jealousy at some time in our lives, but others have a much more predominant jealous streak in their make-up.

How jealous are you? Answer the following questions with yes or no.

1   Are you possessive about your friends?

2   Do you dislike lending your possessions?

4   Do you feel hurt and jealous if your partner looks lust-
     fully at someone on television?

5   Do you feel jealous if you are out with your partner and
     meet one of his/her ex-lovers?

6   Are you upset if friends go out without asking you?

7   Do you feel let down if your pet dog leaves you and
     rushes to someone else, or ignores you and greets your
     partner on your return home?

8   Did you feel as a child that your parents thought more
     of your brother or sister than of you?

9   At school, were you disgruntled if a friend was
     chosen for a sports team, or a part in a play, and you
     weren't?

10   Would you feel angry if you found that your rich next-
     door neighbour had won £150,000?

11   Do you ever feel that a colleague gets more perks than
     you do?

12   Do you feel it is a waste if you see a stunning looking
     girl married to an ugly old man, or a handsome man
     married to an older plain woman?

13   Do you ever feel that other people have all the luck, but
     you have to work hard for everything you get?

14   Have you ever felt envious of a friend's new car?

15   Does it worry you that some people have far more
     money than you have?

16 Do you ever wish you had been born into the Royal Family?

17 If someone complimented your companion on his/ her appearance, and not you, would you feel slighted?

18 If you heard that an old school friend, with fewer qualifications than you, had made a success in business, would you feel jealous?

The Analysis

Give yourself 10 points for every question you answered with YES.

160 - 180   Your eyes must be green you are so jealous. Envious of your own family and fellow employees. Too possessive about your possessions, and probably indulge in long sulks.

100 - 150   You have a marked jealous streak, especially when it comes to people who are better off and seem to have more out of life than you have. You probably complain bitterly about life being unfair.

40 - 90   You have a jealous streak too – though not a very wide one, and you try not to let it show. You feel slighted if other people get more attention than you, but on the whole jealousy is not a problem with you.

30 or less   You are almost too good to be true. Either you have been endowed with wealth, security and

good looks or you really do not have a jealous streak at all. Or you haven't answered the questions truthfully!

14 ARE YOU A MALE CHAUVINIST PIG ?

The Test *(men only)*

In these days of sex equality it is not so easy for a man to reveal himself as an MCP. Let us find out whether you are a male chauvinist pig, and whether you just pay lip-service to the concept of equality.

1 Would you change a baby's nappy?
   a. Only if forced to do so
   b. Yes, certainly
   c. Definitely not!

2 Would you help with the household chores?
   a. Yes, all the time
   b. Only if absolutely forced
   c. Certainly not!

3 Would you cook a meal?
   a. Yes
   b. Only if it was that or starve
   c. Not even if I starved

4 Would you help with the grocery shopping?
   a. Yes, always *b.* Definitely not *c.* Occasionally

5   Do you demand sex from your partner because it is her duty?
    a. Yes *b.* Never *c.* Sometimes

6   Do you think women should have equal pay for equal work?
    a. Yes *b.* No *c.* Sometimes

7   Do you think married women should stay at home and look after the house?
    a. Yes *b.* No *c.* If the husband earns enough

8   Would you go to a lady doctor?
    a. Yes
    b. No
    c. As long as it was nothing too personal

9   Do you open doors for women?
    a. Yes *b.* Never *c.* Only when out with others

10 Would you offer your seat to a woman standing in a train?
    a. Yes, automatically
    b. Only if she was old and frail
    c. No – this is an age of equality

11 Do you take your wife a cup of tea in bed?
    a. Yes *b.* Only at week-ends *c.* Never

12 Do you think a man should be allowed to have a mistress because he has a greater sexual need than women?
    a. Definitely
    b. Certainly not
    c. Only in certain cases

The Analysis

1.	a - 2	2.	b - 2	3.	b - 2
	c - 3		c - 3		c - 3

4.	b - 3	5.	a - 3	6.	b - 3
	c - 2		c - 2		c - 3

7.	a - 3	8.	b - 3	9.	b - 3
	c - 2		c - 2		c - 3

10.	b - 2	11.	b - 2	12.	a - 3
	c - 3		c - 3		c - 3

30 - 36 Make sure you haven't already sprouted a curly tail – you are a first class MCP and a martyr to your own ego, which is monumental. Any woman prepared to put up with you must be a saint or a doormat.

18 - 28 You have a marked chauvinist streak and probably do not agree with sex equality. You prefer women to be submissive and be kept in what you consider to be their place. You would prefer a wife who is prepared to dance attendance on you and any woman who does so is a fool.

6 - 16 You are not a chauvinist pig, but you do have a sneaking feeling that men are superior to women; you don't approve of liberation for women, but do not object to women working.

5 or less You're a nice chap at heart and treat a woman as an equal human being. You have great respect for women and do not treat them as sex objects.

15 WHAT IS YOUR HONESTY RATING ?

The Test

The opinion others have of you is certain to be influenced by your honesty rating, One proverb says 'No man ever got rich by being honest', yet another one tells us that at the end of the day God will look for clean hands, not full ones.

How do you fare in the honesty stakes?

1 If you saw a purse or wallet lying in the road, would you:
   a. Take it to the police station?
   b. Pick it up and take it home?
   c. Ask people around if it is theirs, and if not, keep it?

2 Have you ever taken anything from a shop without paying for it?
   a. Once b. More than once c. Never

3 If you knocked over a vase in someone's home, would you:
   a. Own up straight away?
   b. Blame the cat?
   c. Deny all knowledge?

4 Have you ever accidentally-on-purpose omitted to put down something on your income tax return?
   a. Once   b. More than once c. Never

5 Have you ever feigned illness to get off work?
   a. Once b. Frequently c. Never

6   If you were buying two items in a shop and were only charged for one, would you point it out and pay the correct amount?
a. Yes *b.* No

 If you were brought the wrong bill in a restaurant, and the bill you were given was less than yours, would you:
a. Point it out to the waiter?
b. Quickly pay and get out?
c. Pay it and casually stroll out, saying, if asked, that you hadn't noticed?

8   Have you ever given the impression that you are better off than you actually are?
a. Yes, often *b.* Occasionally *c.* Never

9   If you knew that someone was open to bribery, would you make an attempt to bribe him?
a. Yes, if I was going to gain
b. No, never
c. Yes, if I knew I'd get what I wanted

10   If you bought a coat and accidentally made a mark on it, would you:
a. Keep the coat and try and remove the mark?
b. Take the coat back to the shop and complain that there was a mark on it?
c. Take the coat back saying it was the wrong size, and ask for your money back or an exchange without mentioning the mark?

The Analysis

Give yourself 3 points for each correct answer.

1.	a	2.	c	3.	a	4.	c	5.	c
6.	a	7.	a	8.	c	9.	b	10.	a

24 - 30 You are a very honest person and completely trustworthy. You dislike dishonesty in others and fear to be deceived. Sometimes you can be too suspicious, but your conscience would never allow you to enjoy ill-gotten gains.

9 - 21 You have a dishonest streak in you. You do not consciously set out to deceive, but if the situation arises and you are presented with an opportunity to gain from another's oversight, you are capable of taking advantage.

6 or less You are quite untrustworthy and one of these days you'll get caught.

16 HOW TACTFUL ARE YOU ?

The Test

Tact is knowing which door to enter and saying the right thing at the right time. A lack of this quality has the effect of an axe on an embroidery frame, and can lose you more friends than any social disability.

To find out how tactful you are, answer the following questions.

1 If an elderly lady arrived at your dinner party wearing a dress much too young for her, would you:
   a. Tell her she looked like mutton dressed as lamb?
   b. Glare at the garment in distaste and say, 'Are you sure you'll be warm enough in that dress?'?
   c. Say nothing about the dress and introduce her to your other guests?

2 You have to visit a man in hospital who is very ill. Do you:

    a. Talk very quietly, telling him he mustn't worry and that his family will be looked after when he's gone?

    b. Laugh and tell jokes and say things like, 'As soon as you're better . . . '?

    c. Talk normally, avoiding morbid subjects?

3 At a party you overhear someone talking about something you know is untrue and could be hurtful if the information was wrongly given. Do you:

    a. Dash up and say, 'You're telling it all wrong . . . '?

    b. Ignore it and say nothing?

    c. Go up and excuse yourself saying, 'Do forgive me for butting in, but I couldn't help overhearing your conversation, and I happen to know . . . '?

4 Unbeknown to other guests at your party, one of your friends has recently lost her husband in a plane crash. Suddenly your guests start discussing plane crashes. Do you:

    a. Say: 'Yes, Mary lost her husband in a plane crash recently, so she knows all about it'?

    b. Say: 'Mary's husband was killed in a plane crash recently, would you please discuss something else'?

    c. Change the subject by talking about the time you flew to America and the wonderful holiday you had?

5 You do not like eating kidney and arrive at a small dinner party to find you are given a kidney casserole. Do you:

    a. Say you are sorry, but you don't like kidney?

    b. Eat everything else and leave the kidney, hoping no-one will notice?

    c. Take only a very little kidney and plenty of everything else and eat it, suffering in silence?

6   You meet somebody in the street who obviously knows
    you well, but whose name you cannot remember. Do
    you:
    a. Say 'Sorry I don't remember you'?
    b. Say 'I do hope you will forgive me, I remember
    you so well, but I've got a dreadful memory for
    names . . . '?
    c. Keep up the conversation, hoping that eventually
    something will reveal the person's identity?

7   Someone at work is unsuitable for the job and it is up to
    you to tell them so. Do you:
    a. Say 'I'm sorry, but you're useless at your job'?
    b. Say 'It has fallen to me to have the unpleasant task
    of telling you that the company are not entirely
    happy with your work'?
    c. Say 'I can see you are not happy in your work, and
    we would like to help. What is the problem?'?

8   Your neighbour has had your lawnmower for six
    months. Do you go round and say:
    a. 'I've come for my lawnmower back'?
    b. 'Can I borrow MY lawnmower'?
    c. 'I want to cut my lawn, I wondered if you still have
    my mower'?

9   An elderly relative who visits you twice a year gives
    you a hideous vase as a present. Do you:
    a. Only get it out when she comes, putting it in her
    room?
    b. Give it away and tell her it got broken?
    c. Dispose of it and say absolutely nothing about it?

10 Someone to whom you have forgotten to send a Christ-
    mas card sends one to you. Do you:

43

a. Write one and send it at the last minute?

b. Ignore it and send them one next year?

c. Send your card with a little note, apologising for the lateness, saying you've been late getting your cards out this year?

The Analysis

Give yourself 5 points for each of the following answers.

1. c	2. c	3. c	4. c	5. c
6. b	7. c	8. c	9. a (filled) with flowers)	10. c

45 - 50 You are a tactful and considerate person and manage to say the right thing at the right time. You would hate to cause offence and always take the most polite and inoffensive approach.

30 - 40 On the whole you are tactful, but slip up sometimes, Fortunately you know what the most tactful line is.

10 - 25 There is a difference between being honest and 'saying what you think' and being brutal and hurting someone's sensitive feelings. Try and learn the difference.

5 or less You would appear to be as subtle as a bulldozer. You must charge around giving offence wherever you tread.

17   ARE YOU HONEST WITH YOURSELF ?

The Test

'To thine own self be true' wrote William Shakespeare, and however honest we may be with others, there are times when we try and deceive ourselves. How you evaluate yourself will show by the results of this test.

1   Do you think that you are outstandingly beautiful or very handsome?
   a. Yes *b*. No

2   Do you think you have above average intelligence?
   a. Yes *b*. No

3   Do you ever feel that it is you against the world and other people aren't pulling their weight?
   a. Yes *b*. No

4   Can you list at least four people who have had a great influence in your life ?
   a. Yes *b*. No

5   Do you feel that your parents or guardians had the greatest influence in your life, either negative or positive?
   a. Yes *b*. No

6   Can you laugh at yourself when you make a *faux pas*?
   a. Yes *b*. No

7   Are you able to make a list of your faults?
   a. Yes *b*. No

8 Do you know which aspects of your character irritate others?
   a. Yes *b*. No

9 Can you stop yourself falling in love?
   a. Yes *b*. No

10 Do you ever have any regrets?
   a. Yes *b*. No

11 Do you strive to be successful in everything?
   a. Yes *b*. No

12 Do you strive to make yourself popular?
   a. Yes *b*. No

The Analysis

Give yourself ONE point for each answer that agrees with the following.

1 NO   It is not for you to think you are stunning; if you think so you are either very conceited, or you are deceiving yourself. The greatest beauties of the world are often critical of the way they look.

2 NO   It is not easy to assess what is 'average' intelligence, let alone 'above average'. If you think you are cleverer than others, you might be a bit of a know-all.

3 NO   If you think other people aren't pulling their weight, perhaps you are shifting responsibility, are quick to blame others, and are not honest about your own capabilities.

4 YES   We all have people who have influenced us, and should not deny our debt to them. Parents, teachers, even a filmstar may have influenced different aspects of our outlook.

5 YES   Whoever looked after you in your formative years, whether you like it or not, had the greatest influence on you, from toilet training to how to speak.

6 YES   If you have the ability to laugh at yourself then you are clearly able to take an honest opinion of yourself.

7 YES   To accept and know your faults shows acute knowledge of yourself. To ignore them is not being honest.

8 YES   Again, if you know what aspects of your character are irritating you are honest with yourself.

9 NO   If you are honest with yourself you will know that the one thing you cannot control is human emotion.

10 YES   Most people have some regrets in their life, but to dwell on the past is futile.

11 NO   To strive for success in all things will only lead to disappointments, so learn to accept some failure, which is part of the human condition.

12 NO   If you are honest with yourself you will know that it is possible to try and make yourself popular by being what you are not. Be yourself.

12   You are totally honest with yourself. You have a sensible and open attitude, knowing and accepting your faults, and respecting the influence of other people.

9 - 11   You know yourself well and can be calm and honest about your personality. You don't pretend to yourself that you are anything you are not.

4 - 8   You are not prepared to accept your faults. This could colour other people's attitude towards you, because if you cannot accept yourself, how honest are you going to be towards them?

3 - 0   You are deluding yourself and do not try to see yourself as you really are. You put on your rose-coloured glasses before you look in a mirror and get a distorted picture. Self-respect is good and wholesome, narcissism is not.

18   HOW STRONG IS YOUR CHARACTER ?

The Test

'If we are strong, our character will speak for itself. If we are weak, words will be of no help.'

JOHN F. KENNEDY 1963

Strength of character has nothing to do with big muscles or the ability to lift 200 lb with ease; nor does it mean you are domineering, aggression often being a sign of weakness. Sometimes the most gentle people have the strongest characters.

How does yours compare?

1 Do you know what you want and stick by your decisions?
   a. Yes *b*. No

2 Are you able to remain calm in a crisis?
   a. Yes *b*. No

3 Are you able to smile and cheer up others, even though your own heart is heavy?
   a. Yes *b*. No

4 Do you have the willpower to refuse sweets or alcohol when you know you've had enough?
   a. Yes *b*. No

5 Would you have the control to say No to a physical relationship if you believed your friendship with the person would be threatened?
   a. Yes *b*. No

6 Do you admire self-discipline in others?
   a. Yes *b*. No

7 Does pain in those you love hurt you just as much?
   a. Yes *b*. No

8 Does it upset you to see others unhappy?
   a. Yes *b*. No

9 Do you prefer to do things for others without praise or acknowledgement?
   a. Yes *b*. No

10   Are you able to apologise if you know you are in the wrong?
     a. Yes *b*. No

11   Do you like to be independent and not rely on others?
     a. Yes *b*. No

12   If someone deliberately tries to irritate you, are you
     able to keep your temper?
     a. Yes *b*. No

13   If you thought someone was being particularly selfish
     and causing pain to others could you tell them so?
     a. Yes *b*. No

14   Would you be able to break the news to a friend that
     someone close to them had died?
     a. Yes *b*. No

15   Seeing people less fortunate than yourself, are you
     moved by a desire to help?
     a. Yes *b*. No

The Analysis

Give yourself 10 points for each YES answer.

130 - 150   You are a very strong character and are un-
              selfish in your words and deeds. You often put
              others before yourself, and are prepared to make
              sacrifices if others will benefit.

90 - 120   You are a nice person and are willing to help
              people when you can. You care about other
              people and it pains you to see them unhappy.
              You can speak your mind when necessary, and
              can be relied on in a crisis.

30 - 80 You have quite a strong character, but a slightly selfish streak. You like your creature comforts but would hesitate to give things up to others, although you are prepared to help when you can.

0 - 20 You have a weak character and are open to temptation. You are not prepared to put yourself out to help others if it means being deprived or inconvenienced yourself. You are a poor loser and your first consideration is always Number One.

19 ARE YOU AFRAID TO BE INDIVIDUAL ?

The Test

The confidence to behave how we would really like to is something that not many people possess. Many of us long sometimes to wear outrageous clothes, dance in the streets, make stunning entrances at parties, or sail around the world in a bathtub, but how many have the nerve?

Are you afraid to be an individualist, or are you the person you want to be?

1 Do you dislike routine of any kind?
   a. Yes *b*. Don't mind *c*. Love routine

2 If you had a favourite evening dress and wanted to wear it for a party but weren't sure if other people were dressing up, would you:

a. Still wear it?

b. Wear it, but take a change of clothing with you?

c. Wear something suitable for any occasion?

3   If someone makes a claim which you strongly object to, do you:

a. Tell him so straight away?

b. Tell him quietly when you are alone?

c. Say nothing?

4   Do you have a career that is usually associated with the opposite sex, eg a female motor mechanic, a male midwife?

a. Yes

b. The job is unisex

c. No, it is definitely a job for my own sex

5   Do you enjoy cooking exotic and strange dishes at your parties?

a. Yes, I do

b. No, I prefer to do something simple

c. I don't give parties

6   Do you have any unusual pets – a snake or a tame ferret?
a. Yes *b.* No

7   Are you prepared to stick up for causes you believe in?
a. Yes *b.* No

8   Would you wear something unfashionable because you felt comfortable and looked good in it?
a. Yes *b.* No

9   Would you adopt a special diet if you thought it would do you good?
a. Yes *b.* No

10 Do you find people with conservative tastes boring?
    a. Yes *b.* Most *c.* Not at all

11 Do you have an unusual hobby, such as sky-diving or
    keeping sharks?
    a. Yes *b.* No

12 If you were offered a trip to Australia tomorrow, all
    expenses paid, would you:
    a. Say yes immediately?
    b. Ask them to delay it while you thought it over?
    c. Refuse to go?

The Analysis

Give yourself 5 points for each answer that agrees with the
following.

1. a   2. a   3. a   4. a   5. a   6. a

7. a   8. a   9. a   10. a   11. a   12. a

50 - 60 You are an individualist and have your own
           unique personality and you like people to accept
           you for what you are. You are not bothered about
           what people say about you.

30 - 45 You like to think you are individual, but you tend
           to be just a little reserved and it does worry you
           sometimes what people may think. Inside you are
           an extrovert and there are times when you let it
           show.

10 - 25 You prefer to be one of the crowd and conform.
           Given the choice of a Harvey Wallbanger and a gin
           and orange, you know which you would choose.

5 or less Definitely a conformist, preferring routine and order to anything eccentric or flamboyant. You would hate to be the odd one out, and would never be seen at a party wearing an outfit which could cause eyebrows to lift.

20   HOW MUCH OF A SNOB ARE YOU ?

The Test

A snob is a clique of one person, a person who thinks that he is socially superior to everyone else. Snobs don't try and keep up with the Joneses, they *are* the Joneses.

How much of a snob are you?

1   Would you forego a holiday in Bognor or Cleethorpes simply because you would feel embarrassed to let your trendy friends know?
a. Yes *b*. No

2   Do you ever buy a newspaper, such as the *Guardian*, just to impress other people, when you really prefer the *Sun*?
a. Yes *b*. No

3   Do you prefer large cars to small ones?
a. Yes *b*. No

4   Is it your ambition to be invited to a garden party at Buckingham Palace?
a. Yes *b*. No

5 If you meet someone famous, do you enjoy telling people about it?
a. Yes *b*. No

6 Do you prefer to travel first class rather than second class?
a. Yes *b*. No

7 Do you prefer to buy your clothes from a top store, rather than a familiar chain store?
a. Yes *b*. No

8 Do you prefer to have the most expensive of everything, even though a cheaper version would suit you just as well?
a. Yes *b*. No

9 Do you speak with a slightly 'posher' voice on the telephone?
a. Yes *b*. No

10 Do you wear old school ties, badges or medals at times other than reunions?
a. Yes *b*. No

11 Do you find that some people have an inferior lifestyle to your own?
a. Yes *b*. No

12 Do you have special names for manual workers, such as 'cleaning operative' or 'refuse disposal operative'?
a. Yes *b*. No

23 Have you ever transferred a purchase from a Woolworths bag to a Harrods bag?
a. Yes *b*. No

14 Are you ever worried about 'what the neighbours might think'?
   a. Yes *b.* No

The Analysis

Snob value is rated by the number of YES answers.

If you answered YES to 12 or more questions then you are an outright snob. You have a servile respect for wealth and status, and an exaggerated regard for social position higher than your own. You attempt to cultivate 'gentility' hoping to push yourself into the upper class bracket.

If you scored between 7 - 11, you are still a snob and have an inflated sense of your own importance. It matters terribly what people think of you and you will go out of your way to make sure the opinion is good.

If you scored 1 - 6, well you still have a snobbish streak, although this only applies to certain things, perhaps possessions, or achievements. Not so much a social climber, but you like to think you are respected.

21   ARE YOU QUICK IN A CRISIS ?

The Test

Whatever the crisis, speed is usually the essence. Presence of mind could make the difference between life and death.

Discover how quick-witted you are and how you would react in a crisis. You must do the whole test in less than five minutes.

1   You are walking along the street when you see flames coming from a house, do you:

a. Dash in and try and put the fire out?

b. Knock on the doors of surrounding houses and get a neighbour with a hosepipe?

c. Ring the Fire Brigade, then call on the neighbours to find out if they know whether there is anybody in the house?

2 You are in a compartment on a train and the lady opposite you collapses, do you:

a. Pull the communication cord?

b. Run to find a guard?

c. Go through the train asking if there is a doctor?

3 An elderly person stands too close to a fire and her skirt catches alight, do you:

a. Beat the flames with a newspaper to put them out?

b. Throw cold water over her?

c. Throw a blanket over her and roll her in it?

4 You witness a robbery at a jewellers, do you:

a. Run after the villains?

b. Chase after them in your car?

c. Take their number and call the police?

5 A large dog has its foot caught in some barbed wire, do you:

a. Go up and try to free it?

b. Look for the owner?

c. Call a vet and talk soothingly to the dog until the vet arrives?

6 You enter your office to find that your neurotic secretary is teetering on the window ledge, having decided life is no longer worth living, do you:

a. Call her soothingly and talk to her about it?

b. Tip-toe up behind her and try and grab her?

c. Rush over as fast as you can and try and pull her in?

7   You are driving along the road and come across an icy patch and skid, do you:

a. Jam your brakes on hard?

b. Turn in the opposite direction to which you skid?

c. Turn into the skid?

8   Someone cuts an artery and bright red blood spurts out, do you:

a. Call a doctor and wait until he arrives?

b. Press your thumbs on to the nearest pressure point and get someone to put on a tight bandage before calling a doctor?

c. Ring the doctor, lie the patient down and press a towel against the wound while you wait?

9   A man gets a severe electric shock, do you?

a. Leave him and call a doctor?

b. Lie him on his back, call a doctor and try artificial respiration?

c. Lie him on his front, arms across forehead, head to one side. Try artificial respiration. Call the doctor?

10   A child swallows something that might be poisonous, do you:

a. Watch for any pain?

b. Take the child to a doctor?

c. Give the child salt water to make him vomit. Seek medical advice?

The Analysis

Give yourself 10 points for each correct answer.

1 c   The most important thing is to call the Fire Brigade before doing anything else. They will be there within minutes. Don't go into the house, there could be an explosion from gas

2 c   Look for a doctor. If you pull the communication cord the train could stop in the middle of nowhere, and there could be medical help at the next station

3 c   A blanket will suffocate the flames and put them out at once

4 c   Never chase – you could be shot or badly hurt

5 c   Try and calm the dog, but don't touch it, it will be shocked and could turn vicious. If you tried to disentangle it yourself you could hurt the dog as well as risk being bitten

6 a   Never try and grab the person suddenly as the shock could send them over the edge

7 c   Turn the same way as the skid

8 b   The important thing is to apply pressure immediately, even before calling the doctor

9 c   Don't lie the person on their back, they could vomit and choke. Get medical help immediately. Turn over and massage the heart if necessary

10 c   Make the child sick. Any delay could be dangerous

70 - 100	You are very quick in a crisis and a useful person to have around.
40 - 60	You probably know the theory of what to do but are likely to panic.
30 or less	I wouldn't want to be in a difficult situation with you! At least, having done this test, you now know what you should do.

22 ARE YOU A PRUDE ?

The Test

'Nature knows no indecencies; Man invents them.'

MARK TWAIN

A certain amount of modesty is one thing – prudery another. You may not think you are a prude, but do you feel uncomfortable at the sight of a naked thigh, or blush when a man's briefs are a little too brief?

1   If you walk around after you have had a bath, do you wear a towel around your middle:
a. If you are alone?
b. If your partner is there?
c. If members of the family are around?

2   If your partner walked around the house naked would you feel embarrassed?
a. Yes *b.* If other people were there *c.* No.

3   Would you sunbathe naked in your garden if it were not overlooked?

a. No
b. Yes, on my own
c. Yes, even with other people

4   Would you take a holiday at a nudist camp?
    a. Yes, if my partner agreed
    b. Yes, even if I went alone
    c. Never

5   Do you find topless waitresses disgusting?
    a. Yes *b*. If my family were with me *c*. No

6   If a forthcoming programme on television announced
    that it contained something explicitly sexual, would
    you:
    a. Watch it with an open mind?
    b. Turn off and write a letter of complaint?
    c. Switch off and feel disgusted that such material is
        allowed on TV?

7   Would you feel embarrassed if a child asked you a
    question about sex?
    a. Definitely
    b. Yes, if it was a young child
    c. Not at all, I believe in honesty

8   Do you ever think of your parents having sex?
    a. Yes, why shouldn't they?
    b. I'm sure they don't
    c. It disgusts me even to think about it

8   Would you go and see an 'X' certificate film?
    a. Never
    b. If I knew the story and why it had been given an 'X'
        certificate
    c. Yes, certainly

10 Do you think all homosexual relationships should be made completely illegal?
a. Definitely
b. Certainly not
c. Not illegal, but 21 should remain the age of consent

The Analysis

Give yourself 5 points for each of the following answers:

1. c   2. c   3. c   4. a or b   5. c

6. a   7. c   8. a   9. c   10. b

40 - 50   You are not a prude at all, in fact you can be quite immodest at times. A naked body does not embarrass you, although you might feel abashed if your children, or a maiden aunt, saw you naked. You have an open mind and can be honest with yourself and others.

25 - 35   Naked bodies do not offend you, but sex should be a private matter and you do not like to discuss the subject. You can be open and honest with your partner, but embarrassed if other people wish to discuss their sex life with you.

5 - 20   You are too modest and easily disgusted. You find naked bodies offensive and would not talk openly about sex; you would even feel embarrassed talking to your doctor about a sexual problem.

0   You are an absolute prude – you always undress in the dark (after throwing a cover over the budgie's cage), and I expect you've got your piano legs covered up.

23 ARE YOU A TOLERANT PERSON ?

The Test

We are often judged by how tolerant we are, especially of minorities, and the way in which we react to them. If we accept people for what they are and tolerate things which we may not like, we are liked and trusted ourselves, and gain respect.

This test will help show how tolerant you are.

1 If you found that your son or daughter was having a homosexual relationship, would you find it easy to accept?
   a. Yes, I would understand
   b. No, I would find it difficult to come to terms with

2 Do you think that women should be ordained as Bishops?
   a. Yes, if qualified *b*. No

3 Are you racially prejudiced?
   a. Yes *b*. No

4 If your son or daughter wished to marry a coloured person (or a white person if you are coloured), would you be in agreement?
   a. Yes *b*. No

5 Would you accept a coloured female pope?
   a. Yes *b*. Definitely not

6 Do you accept the fact that some people are clairvoyant and that mediums can communicate with the dead?
   a. Yes *b*. No

7 Do you feel that the age of consent for homosexuals should be lowered?
a. Yes *b.* No

8 Do you listen to Party Political Broadcasts by parties other than the one you support?
a. Yes *b.* Never

9 If you were interviewing someone for a job, and although qualified in all respects, they looked like a punk rocker, would you give them the job?
a. Yes *b.* No

10 Do you think that life today is better than it has ever been?
a. Yes *b.* No, things have never been so bad

11 If the government announced they were going to spend £2 million on research into UFOs would you feel it was money wasted?
a. No *b.* Yes

12 Do you think people can be Christians without going to church?
a. Yes *b.* No

13 Does the attitude towards sex in the eighties show a decline in moral standards?
a. No *b.* Yes

14 If it was proposed to open a sex shop in your town, would you object?
a. No *b.* Yes

The Analysis

Questions 1 and 2:   a = 1 point
Question 3:   b = 1 point
Questions 6 - 14:   a = 1 point

12 - 14   You are an extremely tolerant person, perhaps too tolerant at times, and do not make objections when you ought. Either you do not care what goes on around you, or you are sexually permissive yourself and are prepared to accept anything.

8 - 11   You are tolerant and forgiving, prepared to accept people's weaknesses, and probably aware of your own weaknesses too. You are a progressive thinker and prepared to accept change, so long as it will improve life.

5 - 7   You are not as tolerant as you might be, and have set views from which you will not budge. You find it difficult to tolerate minorities and do not accept change willingly. You think your own high standards should be adhered to.

4 or less   You are very intolerant and at times much too self-righteous. Your approach to life is inflexible and you are probably very bigoted. Perhaps you mutter under your breath 'I don't know what the world/ the young/morals are coming to'.

24   ARE YOU A SEX MANIAC ?

The Test

The playwright Richard Brinsley Sheridan wrote that 'nothing is unnatural that is not physically impossible'. Yet many people are sexually unadventurous and will not indulge in certain activities because it is considered 'unnatural'.

Are you adventurous to the extent of becoming a sex maniac or are you an 'in' person who believes sex should be *in* bed, *in* the dark, *in* one position, and *in* frequently?

Below is a list of sexual activities. Beside each one write a number 3 if you have enjoyed doing this frequently; number 2 if you've tried it; number 1 if you've only thought about it; and 0 if you wouldn't consider it.

1   Oral sex
2   Anal sex
3   Group sex
4   Sex with a younger partner
5   Sex with an older partner
6   Sex with men
7   Sex with women
8   Sex with two others
9   Voyeurism
10   Transvestism
11   Masturbation
12   Exhibitionism
13   Fantasising
14   Interracial sex
15   Bondage
16   Masochism
17   Sadomasochism
18   Watching pornography
19   Taking part in an orgy

20   Sex in bath/shower
21   Extramarital sex
22   Use of sex toys/aids
23   Dressing up
24   Sex in a plane

The Analysis

0 - 24   You either have a very active imagination or are completely turned off by sex of any kind. Either way your sex life is meagre, and you no doubt find a physical relationship abhorrent. Perhaps you need therapy to overcome your inhibitions.

25 - 48   You are prepared to try anything once. You may not have a very satisfactory sex life, perhaps you cannot find the partner that you are completely in tune with, or are not prepared to settle for simple sexual activity.

49 - 60   You are quite happy with your sex life and are about average in that you have tried various activities and you know what you like and what you don't. Sex is an important part of a relationship for you, and you have an open mind.

61 - 72   You must be exhausted, practically everything turns you on, and you can be classed as a Sex Maniac. As long as you've been honest and haven't fantasised in this test, you must be a superstud – and possibly a menace.

25   ARE YOU AN ALCOHOLIC ?

The Test

Of course you're not – the potential alcoholic never is in his or her own estimation. But answer yes or no to the following questions honestly and find out:

1   Do you lose time from work due to drinking?

2   Is drinking making your home life unhappy?

3   Do you drink because you're shy with other people?

4   Is drinking affecting your reputation?

5   Have you ever felt remorse after drinking?

6   Have you ever been in financial difficulties as a result of drinking?

7   Do you turn to lower companions and an inferior environment when drinking?

8   Does your drinking make you careless of your family's welfare?

9   Has your ambition decreased since drinking?

10   Do you crave a drink at a definite time daily?

11   Do you want a drink the next morning?

12   Does drinking cause you to have difficulty in sleeping?

13   Has your efficiency decreased since drinking?

14 Is drinking jeopardising your job or business?

15 Do you drink to escape from worries or trouble?

16 Do you drink alone?

17 Have you ever had a complete loss of memory as a result of drinking?

18 Has your doctor ever treated you for drinking?

19 Do you drink to build up your self-confidence?

20 Have you ever been to a hospital or institution on account of drinking?

The Analysis

If you answered YES to any *one* of the questions, there is a definite warning that you may be an alcoholic.

If you answered YES to any *two*, the chances are you are an alcoholic.

If you answered YES to THREE or more, you are definitely an alcoholic.

26 ARE YOU A LION OR A MOUSE ?

The Test

What do you do if you hear screams at night – or noises in the house? Do you argue with your boss?

This test will tell you how you rate in the pecking-order of life's jungle.

1   As you are turning in for the night, you hear screams in the street; do you:
    a. Call the police?
    b. Go to bed?
    c. Arm yourself with a hammer and go outside to help?

2   A pair of shoes you bought a week ago are falling apart; would you:
    a. Make a loud complaint in the shop on a busy afternoon?
    b. Accept it as today's shoddy workmanship?
    c. Ask to see the shop manager and tell him the trouble?

3   When a restaurant bill or a bank statement arrives, do you:
    a. Run through it quickly to see if it looks right?
    b. Put your faith in computers?
    c. Check every item?

4   You are waiting to pay for something in a shop, but the assistant keeps on chatting with a colleague. Do you:
    a. Summon the manager?
    b. Go to another shop?
    c. Interrupt the conversation?

5   If you saw a child being violently slapped by its mother, would you:
    a. Ignore it?
    b. Approach the woman and ask her to stop?
    c. Get the nearest policeman?

6   You are in a non-smoking carriage on a train and someone lights a cigarette. Do you:

a. Ask them to put it out and point to the sign?

b. Leave the carriage?

c. Report it to the guard?

7 In a friendly tennis match, are you:

   a. Hitting every ball as if you were at Wimbledon?

   b. Just enjoying the game?

   c. Letting the other person win?

8 You are walking by a swimming pool when a stranger pushes you in. Do you:

   a. Get out and push them in?

   b. Report them to the attendant?

   c. Swim off?

9 Your boss has passed a rule that you think is nonsense. Do you:

   a. Abide by it anyway?

   b. Try to persuade him to change his mind?

   c. Break the rule when he is not there?

10 A popular member of your local club has been fiddling the accounts, but you know that reporting it will make *you* unpopular. Do you:

   a. Have a quiet word with the person yourself?

   b. Say nothing?

   c. Report the offender to the committee?

11 At a celebration dinner, the meat is burnt and the vegetables soggy. Do you:

   a. Resolve never to go back to the restaurant again?

   b. Ask the head waiter to bring you another meal?

   c. Refuse to pay after you have finished?

12 If a doctor prescribes you tablets, do you:

a. Ask him what they are for, and all about side-effects?
b. Take them?
c. Ask for a second opinion?

13 You are driving normally when you see a policeman behind you, Do you:
a. Carry on as you are? *b*. Slow down? *c*. Speed up?

14 In a relationship, do you prefer to be:
a. Equal? *b*. Dominant? *c*. The underdog?

15 You are on your own in the house when you think you hear a noise upstairs. Do you:
a. Investigate on your own?
b. Get a neighbour to investigate with you?
c. Go and stay with a friend?

16 You are with a group of friends who cannot decide what to do for the evening. Would you:
a. Go along with everyone else?
b. Make a few suggestions?
c. Say 'Come on everybody, follow me'?

17 Your next door neighbour asks you to look after her cats for a week, but you are allergic to them. Do you:
a. Say no?
b. Suffer in silence for a week?
c. Explain the problem and suggest someone else?

18 In a debate, do you:
a. Speak your true feelings?
b. Make your point at any cost?
c. Keep quiet?

19 Someone is telling you the same story for the tenth time. Do you:

a. Try to look interested?

b. Yawn and say, 'Not again'?

c. Mention that you think you've heard it before?

20 Somebody at the next table to you in a restaurant is explaining something, but you can hear they are wrong. Do you:

a. Say nothing?

b. Go and put them right?

c. Mention it to your companions only?

The Analysis

1.	a - 5	2.	a - 10	3.	a - 5	4.	a - 10
	b - 0		b - 0		b - 0		b - 0
	c - 10		c - 5		c - 10		c - 5

5.	a - 0	6.	a - 5	7.	a - 10	8.	a - 10
	b - 10		b - 0		b - 5		b - 5
	c - 5		c - 10		c - 0		c - 0

9.	a - 0	10.	a - 5	11.	a - 0	12.	a - 5
	b - 5		b - 0		b - 5		b - 0
	c - 10		c - 10		c - 10		c - 10

13.	a - 5	14.	a - 5	15.	a - 10	16.	a - 0
	b - 0		b - 10		b - 5		b - 5
	c - 10		c - 0		c - 0		c - 10

17.	a - 10	18.	a - 5	19.	a - 0	20.	a - 0
	b - 0		b - 10		b - 10		b - 10
	c - 5		c - 0		c - 5		c - 5

140 - 200   Well, you're the king of the jungle. No-one within 100 miles can make a decision without you interfering. If people give in to you you can be sure it's for the sake of keeping the peace.

70 - 135   You will not let anybody run your life for you –
           live and let live is your motto. Friends can count
           on you and you can always get your point across
           without being offensive.

0 - 65   You are so afraid of being unpopular you are
           scared to open your mouth. But by playing it so
           softly, you are liable to be overlooked altogether.
           Stand up for yourself and others – it will earn
           you a lot more respect.

27   DO YOU FEEL INSECURE ?

The Test

A feeling of insecurity can stem from a long forgotten
incident in childhood, such as the time you got separated
from your mother in Woolworths, and thought you had
been abandoned, or it can be the very real memory of a
painful event in later life.

The following questions will help to show how secure or
insecure you really are.

1   Do you ever feel incredibly lonely and isolated, even
    though you are rarely alone?
    a. Quite often, especially at night
    b. Only very rarely
    c. Never

2   Do you feel uncomfortable in large houses with
    spacious rooms and very little furniture?
    a. Yes, very uncomfortable
    b. Don't mind big rooms, but prefer a lot of furniture
    c. Love big houses and the sense of freedom

3 Do you worry about the responsibilities you have and wish you could unburden them on to someone else?
   a. Yes, definitely *b.* Only sometimes *c.* Never worry

4 When you are away from home do you worry that someone might break in?
   a. All the time
   b. It occurs to me sometimes
   c. Never think about it

5 At night do you ever worry over the unpleasant incidents that have occurred in your life and relive the past?
   a. Often *b.* Sometimes *c.* Never, what's past is past

6 Do you ever worry about what people may think about you?
   a. Frequently *b.* Occasionally *c.* Never

7 Do you ever feel that people are laughing about you behind your back, even though they probably aren't?
   a. Often *b.* Occasionally *c.* Never

8 Do you ever feel worried about answering the telephone or opening a letter in case it is bad news?
   a. Frequently *b.* Only on odd occasions *c.* Never

9 Would, or does, living in the country make you feel cut off and uncomfortable?
   a. All the time *b.* Only when I'm alone *c.* Never

10 Do you ever feel frightened of the dark?
   a. Always *b.* Sometimes *c.* Never

11 If you are alone in the house do you have the radio, hi-fi or television on for company?

a. Always
b. Sometimes
c. Only if there is something I especially want to listen to.

12 Do you like exploring new places, or do you prefer familiar towns that you know well?
a. Only feel comfortable in places I know well
b. Like exploring if someone is with me
c. Enjoy seeing new places, even if alone

The Analysis

For every 'a' answer give yourself 3 points
For every 'b' answer give yourself 2 points
For every 'c' answer give yourself 1 point

27 - 36 You are very insecure, frightened of the dark and scared of being alone. You would probably feel most secure by a log fire in the arms of the one you love. You like to have your own boundaries and possessions, and see strangers as a threat to your territory.

17 - 26 You are basically a secure person, but still feel uncomfortable sometimes in the presence of strangers, and prefer to have familiar things and people around you. In the past things have happened which you regretted, and dwelling on these adds to your feeling of insecurity.

Under 16 You have no worries about security. You enjoy meeting new people and are content in any surroundings. You quite enjoy being alone at times, enjoying your independence.

28 HOW ECONOMICAL ARE YOU ?

The Test

In these days of limited resources it is necessary for a proper regard to be observed in our spending habits. To test how economical you are in the eighties, or how much of a spend-thrift, answer the following questions.

1 In the evening do you have lights on in parts of the house or in rooms other than the ones occupied?
   a. Frequently *b*. Sometimes *c*. Never

2 Do you ever have lights on unnecessarily during the day when you could manage with daylight?
   a. Quite often *b*. Occasionally *c*. Never

3 Do you squeeze the last bit of toothpaste out of the tube or throw the old one away, knowing there is more to be got but you can't be bothered?
   a. Always *b*. Sometimes *c*. No, I always use every bit

4 Do you ever send unimportant letters by first class mail when you could just as easily send them second class?
   a. Always *b*. Mostly *c*. I always use second class mail

5 If there is just a cupful of cereal left in your cornflake packet, do you throw it away and start a new packet, or use up the old first?
   a. I throw the last bits away
   b. I sometimes use it all
   c. I always eat every morsel

6 Do you heat unoccupied parts of your house in the winter?

a. I always heat the whole house
b. I heat the whole house in the evenings only
c. I only ever have the heat on in the room I am actually in

7   When you wash, do you use a basin full of hot water, or do you allow the hot tap to run endlessly?
a. I allow the tap to run
b. I sometimes allow the tap to run
c. I only use the amount of water I need

8   If you see something on special offer in your shop do you buy several packets or do you just buy one and hope that it will stay low in price?
a. I only buy one packet
b. I buy two packets if it's something I am going to use
c. I buy several packets while it is cheap

9   Do you always buy well-known brand names when you purchase a product, or do you buy the shop's own name brand?
a. I always buy a known brand, even if I pay more
b. I always buy the shop's own because it is cheaper and tastes the same

10 If you buy a joint of meat and there is more than enough, do you:
a. Use it all up in one go?
b. Stretch it out and make it last for two meals?

11 Do you always take the car, even on a short journey, when it would be quite easy to walk?
a. I drive everywhere
b. I only walk if I am going a distance less than two streets

c. I only use the car if it is impractical and impossible to walk

12   If you see something in the shops that you do not really need, but it is reduced in price, do you buy it?
a. Always, in case it comes in useful
b. I only buy something if I really need it

The Analysis

Questions 1 - 8   If you answered 'c' give yourself 3 points
If you answered 'b' give yourself 2 points

9.   b - 3   10.   b - 3   11.   c - 3   12.   b - 3

30 - 36   You are very economical and hate needless waste and extravagance. You value your money and have no intention of throwing it around needlessly. With the money you save you can buy things you really want.

21 - 28   You try to be economical in household matters and most of the time succeed, but you are often tempted by bargains that you don't need. You could be just a little more careful with the pennies and save yourself pounds.

Less   You are extravagant and uneconomical, either
than 21   because you feel that you can afford it, or because it has never really entered your head to economise. Perhaps you should budget more carefully.

29   ARE YOU A WINNER OR A DEFEATIST ?

The Test

As individuals, we tend to fall into one of two categories. We move forward to overcome obstacles. Or we retreat, refusing to face up to reality, and taking the easy way out.

Try this test by answering yes or no to discover which category you belong to.

1   You have an inferiority complex regarding your appearance. Would you ask friends to advise you and seek the aid of skilled people, like a good hairdresser?

2   You are nervous about speaking in public. Would you join a drama or discussion group or a public-speaking class?

3   You have suffered an illness or an accident, or acquired a physical disability. Would you concentrate on getting better, if possible, and permit it to interfere with normal life as little as possible?

4   Are difficulties and setbacks challenges that make you want to have another go and do better next time?

5   Can you stand up for yourself and avoid being upset by awkward, rude, hostile, unhelpful people?

6   You have a personal problem, like discovering that a person you love does not love you. Could you face up to the harsh reality of the situation and decide what action to take?

7   A decision you should make will arouse criticism. Would you make it and stick by it?

8   You need the support and co-operation of other people. Some are uninterested and some unwilling to help. Would you persevere in your efforts to win them over?

9   A friend does something you do not approve of or adopts an unpopular attitude. Would you stand by him in the sense of remaining friendly and helpful?

10 You have put your foot in it and made yourself generally unpopular. Could you eat humble pie and apologise?

11 There is an unpleasant job to be done. Are you the type who gets it done as soon as possible?

12 A necessary job is hard, tedious and boring. Would you stick at it until it was finished?

13 You are interested, but your friends are not. Would you go it alone?

14 Your friends are interested, but you are not. Nevertheless, you are becoming involved. Could you say, 'Sorry, there are other things I want to do.'?

15 People are taking you for granted. Could you say, 'Sorry, I'm not available like that all the time.'?

16 You appear to be making no impression. Would this cause you to go out of your way to be extra friendly and helpful?

17 An arrangement falls through. You are disappointed. Would you find something else you could do?

18 Old friends die or move away. Would you continue to go out among people and develop new friendships?

19 You have to change your job or move away. Could you adapt yourself to make the best of it?

20 You have been trying for a long time but seem to have made little progress. Would you try even harder?

The Analysis

Give yourself 5 points for every YES.

70+   This shows that your dominant attitude is to overcome obstacles and not to retreat from them.

60 - 70   This can be counted as good and positive.

50 - 55   Satisfactory.

Less   Not at all satisfactory, and you should aim at being constructive and practical in your approach to life.

30   ARE YOU EFFICIENT ?

The Test

You probably think you are efficient and competent, but you may be in for a surprise.

Tick whichever of the following you think applies to you.

1   *a*. Are you systematic?
    b. Or are you apt to let things slide?

2   *a*. At night do you generally turn in at a set hour?
    b. Or do you often feel too lazy to go to bed?

3   *a*. Do you believe that things are always piling up on you?
    b. Or are you always able to cope with your everyday chores?

4   *a*. Do you enjoy meeting and dealing with the unexpected in your business and/or private affairs?
    b. Or do you easily panic and lose your grip?

5   *a*. Are you inclined to be careless in your dress?
    b. Or do you take care with your appearance, without overdoing it?

6   *a*. Do you ever get your dates mixed up?
    b. Or are you very careful in that respect?

7   *a*. Do you always think before you act?
    b. Or do you rush in where angels fear to tread?

8   *a*. Are you always on time when meeting someone?
    b. Or do you feel that a half-hour difference one way or the other doesn't matter?

9   *a*. Are you always on the lookout for ways and means to improve your work?
    b. Or do you believe that it's too much bother and stick to a fixed routine all the time?

10   *a*. Are you careful in your speech?
    b. Or are you apt to slur your words?

The Analysis

Give yourself 5 points for each answer which agrees with the following:

1. a   2. a   3. b   4. a   5. b

6. b   7. a   8. a   9. a   10. a

40 - 50 You have nothing to worry about, and can be relied upon to keep everything going smoothly and efficiently.

25 - 35 You're a little careless sometimes, but not catastrophically so. You're probably a cheerful live-and-let-live person.

Less We said you could be in for a surprise. The surprise is that you ever get anything done. Pay attention at the back there.

31 HOW WELL DO YOU KNOW YOUR PARTNER ?

The Test

We all think we know our spouses intimately. We know their hopes and desires, their likes and dislikes, and their preferences in all things . . . or do we?

To find out just how well you know your partner, answer the following questions and get him/her to answer the same questions. How well you know your partner depends on how many questions you answer the same.

1 What is your partner's favourite colour?

2 Given the choice of a holiday, which would your partner choose?
   a. A sun soaked beach
   b. Touring/sightseeing
   c. Walking/sporting

3 Given the following choice of dishes in a restaurant, which would your partner choose?
   a. Spaghetti Bolognese
   b. Steak and Kidney Pie
   c. Madras Chicken Curry with rice

4 Which is your partner's favourite meat (that is if he/she is not vegetarian):
   a. Beef *b*. Pork *c*. Lamb

5 Would your partner know the date of Mother's Day?

6 If you were going out for the evening, would your partner choose:
   a. A cosy intimate restaurant
   b. The local pub
   c. The theatre or cinema

7 What is your partner's favourite kind of movie?
   a. Comedy *b*. Historical adventure *c*. Science Fiction

8 Which is the first item of clothing your partner puts on in the morning?
   a. Underclothes *b*. Socks/tights *c*. Shirt/blouse

9 What is your partner's favourite music?
   a. Classical *b*. Rock/pop *c*. Light jazz

10 Do you know your partner's chest/bust measurement –
    what is it?

11 Given a book token, what kind of book would your
    partner choose?
    a. Fiction *b*. Biography *b*. Factual/historical *d*. Others

12 What is your partner's ambition?

13 What shoe size does your partner take?

14 Given the choice of three dogs, which would your
    partner prefer?
    a. Golden Labrador
    b. King Charles Spaniel
    c. West Highland Terrier

The Analysis

If your partner confirms that you answered 12-14 questions correctly, then you know him or her very well indeed, and are either very much in love, or have known each other so long that there is nothing left to know.

If you answered 7-10 questions correctly then you are certainly getting to know your partner well, but still have a lot more to find out, which will probably be a surprise because you thought you knew everything.

If you only got 6 or less right then either you have only just met, or you haven't got to know the person very well. If you've been married twenty years, then shame on you, but if you've only known each other a short time, then you can be forgiven, and should have fun finding out more.

32 HOW SUCCESSFUL IS YOUR MARRIAGE ?

The Test

To make a success of any partnership requires a tremendous amount of give and take on both sides, without which the bed of roses can turn into a battlefield.

Marriage has been described as a feast where 'the grace is sometimes better than the dinner'. Nevertheless, it is an institution which many join and the remainder strive to belong. But what makes a successful marriage?

1 Do you ever think that other couples are probably happier and have a more successful marriage than your own?
   a. Yes *b.* No

2 Do you think that a good sex life is essential to a successful marriage?
   a. Yes *b.* No

3 Do you think a wife should stay at home to create a happy domestic life?
   a. Yes *b.* No

4 Are you able to talk openly to each other about your innermost feelings?
   a. Yes *b.* No

5 Are you embarrassed if your spouse sees you naked?
   a. Yes *b.* No

6 Do you each have different interests and hobbies of your own?
   a. Yes *b.* No

7   If you or your partner are attracted to members of the opposite sex, is it likely to hurt your marriage?
    a. No *b*. Yes

8   Do you ever do things that you do not really enjoy simply to please your partner?
    a. Yes *b*. No

9   If your partner bought a new item of clothing which you considered ridiculous, would you risk upsetting him/her and tell the truth?
    a. Yes *b*. No

10 When there are big decisions to make do you plan them together, and are you influenced by your partner's point of view?
    a. Yes *b*. No

11 Do you always sleep in a double bed?
    a. Yes *b*. No

12 Do you think that the odd argument or disagreement is a threat to your marriage and another step towards divorce?
    a. Yes *b*. No

13 Do you think marriage should be 'till death us do part'?
    a. Yes *b*. No

14 Do you think that your marriage changes for the worse when children are born?
    a. Yes *b*. No

The Analysis

1 b   You cannot judge by outward appearances whether other marriages are more successful than your own. We don't know what happens when the couple are alone.

2 b   A good sex life enhances your marriage, but there are many contented marriages between couples who cannot have sex because of illness or disability.

3 b   No. These days a woman expects more from a marriage than four walls and domestic routine. If both parties share the tedious chores, and bring stimulation from outside the home, it will help to keep the marriage sweet and fresh.

4 a   A husband and wife should feel able to talk openly and honestly to each other.

5 b   No – you should not be at all embarrassed.

6 a   If both man and woman have varied interests it will prevent staleness creeping into the marriage.

7 a   No, of course it won't hurt your marriage if you feel attracted to members of the opposite sex – so long as you behave maturely and make sure to keep your marriage intact.

8 a   Yes, 'give and take' again – and you should be prepared to please your partner.

9 a   Yes, no offence should be taken if the criticism is constructive.

10   a   Yes, any major decisions that concern you both should be arrived at jointly.

11   a   Yes – but it doesn't mean your marriage is on the rocks if you have separate beds. Many people just sleep better on their own.

12   a   All couples argue and so long as the arguments don't escalate into violence or damage the personality, no harm results. But be sure to make up before going to bed each night.

13   a   Of course.

14   b   There are certain to be many changes, but not necessarily for the worse. There are new responsibilities, problems and joys to share.

Give yourself 10 for each correct answer.

110 - 140   Yours is a very successful marriage – no major problems.

60 - 100   Yours is an average marriage – jogging along and compares with most marriages.

20 - 50   You have problems and you both need to work together to overcome the difficulties. More give and take seems called for.

10 or less   See a Marriage Guidance Counsellor.

33 HOW MUCH DO YOU KNOW ABOUT YOUR BODY ?

The Test

You might claim that you know your body intimately, but do you really know as much about the human body as you think you do?

1   In a man weighing 162 lbs, how much water does his body contain?
    a. 3 gallons *b*. 7 gallons *c*. 10 gallons

2   How much of our body weight is muscle?
    a. 67% *b*. 43% *c*. 29%

3   What percentage are bones of our total body weight?
    a. 72% *b*. 47% *c*. 14%

4   What is the average weight of a new born baby?
    a. 6 lb 7 oz *b*. 7 lb 4 oz *c*. 8 lb 2 oz

5   How much blood, approximately, does your heart pump in one day?
    a. 150 gallons *b*. 1000 gallons *c*. 2000 gallons

6   What causes the greatest number of deaths annually?
    a. Cancer *b*. Coronary thrombosis *c*. Accidents

7   Is colour blindness an hereditary defect?
    a. Yes *b*. No

8   From which part of the body is most heat lost?
    a. Through the top of the head
    b. From the chest
    c. Equal amounts are lost from all over

9   How many cells make up the human brain?
    a. 5,000,000 *b*. 10,000,000 *c*. 14,000,000

10   Does everybody dream every night, even if they can't remember it?
    a. Yes *b*. No

11   We consume vast amounts of tea. Is tea –
    a. a nutrient? *b*. a drug? *c*. of no value?

12   How many calories does the average man need to eat each day?
    a. 1650 *b*. 2800 *c*. 3120

13   Is a day-old baby boy capable of having an erection?
    a. Yes *b*. Only in rare cases *c*. No

14   Can hair turn white overnight after severe shock?
    a. Yes *b*. No

15. What is the 'clavicle'?
    a. Collar bone *b*. Shoulder blade *c*. Knee-cap

16   Are twins always born at the same time or can the second twin be born days or weeks later?
    a. Born both together
    b. Always within 24 hours
    c. Can be days later

The Analysis

Give yourself 5 points for each correct answer.

1. a	2. b	3. c	4. b	5. c	6. b
7. a	8. a	9. c	10. a	11. b	12. b
13. a	14. b	15. a	16. c		

60 - 80	Either you are a doctor or you have a very good knowledge of the human body. Well done.
30 - 55	You know your body quite well, but some things puzzle you and amaze you when you know the facts.
5 - 25	Biology is not your strong suit. You can just about tell the difference between male and female.

34 ARE YOU IN TUNE WITH YOUR BODY ?

The Test

Are you in perfect harmony with your body, knowing exactly what it needs, or do you abuse it and then wonder why it lets you down?

Do you like the body you have, or are you embarrassed by it? The human body has always been a controversial subject; we have one or two types, yet the sight of a female breast or a male buttock on television can bring forth howls of protest from 'Disgusted of Tunbridge'.

1   Do you feel embarrassed about seeing yourself naked in the mirror?

2   Do you find parts of your anatomy objectionable?

3   Do you enjoy exploring your body?

4   Are you able to wake up when you want to without an alarm clock?

5 Can you sleep anywhere, anytime?

6 Do you have regular bowel movements, or do you try and adopt your own special times?

7 Do you find bodily functions embarrassing?

8 Are you aware if you have bad breath?

9 Do you wash your hair when it needs washing?

10 Can you feel when you are overweight and do you diet accordingly?

11 Do you ever suffer from spots?

12 If you get a spot, do you apply cream to shift it?

13 Do you know how much sun your body can tolerate and at what point your skin will burn?

14 Do you make sure that your shoes fit perfectly?

15 If you have a cold do you rest more or do you carry on as normal?
   a. Rest more b. Carry on as normal

16 Do you suffer from any allergies, and do you know how to cure them?

17 Do you occasionally try and exercise your body?

18 Do you find it easy to relax?

1   Only prudish or guilty people find their own body
    embarrassing. A normal and healthy attitude is to
    accept it totally. But over-glorification in one's body
    is wrong too.
    Yes - 0   No - 1 point

2   All parts of your body are quite natural and you should
    have no taboo areas.
    No - 1 point   Yes - 0

3   It is natural to be inquisitive about your body and to
    enjoy stroking and feeling it. This can be very sensual
    and comforting, so long as you don't become obsessive
    about it.
    Yes - 1 point   No - 0

4   If you are in control of your body and rest it sufficiently
    you should find it quite easy to wake up without an
    alarm clock.
    Yes - 1 point   No - 0

5   Again, total harmony with yourself and the world will
    enable you to sleep anywhere, anytime. There are,
    however, few people who can just sleep at will and feel
    refreshed afterwards.
    Yes - 1 point   No - 0

6   Regular bowel movements are important – but what is
    regular for you might not be the same for others. One
    should not try to force a timetable of one's own.
    Regular - 1 point   Own timetable - 0

7   Bodily functions are perfectly natural and should not
    be considered as dirty. But neither should you have an
    unhealthy obsession with them.
    Yes - 0   No - 1 point

8   Bad breath can result from many things – often through tooth decay. Halitosis is as much a social as a physical malfunction and it is important to know if your breath is bad. Friends might be too polite to tell you.

    Yes - 1   No - 0

9   The time to wash your hair is just before it needs it.

    Yes - 1   No - 0

10 If you can pinch more than an inch of fat, you are overweight. If you feel breathless and clothes are a tight fit, you are grossly overweight. People in tune with their bodies know when they have eaten too much, and will cut down on the calories.

    Yes - 1 point   No - 0

11 Most of us have spots at some time. It can be due to sebum or clogged pores, and is not necessarily your fault.

    Yes - 1 point   No - 0

12 Antiseptic ointment helps – you should never pick or squeeze as this can lead to infection.

    Yes - 1 point   No - 0

13 Apart from boosting your ego, a suntan does you practically no good at all, and frequent sunburn can be positively harmful and can cause skin cancer. It is wise to know how much you can take before you burn.

    Yes - 1 point   No - 0

14 Ill-fitting shoes can cause serious foot problems and deformities. Never wear shoes that are too small out of vanity.

    Yes - 1 point   No - 0

15   Don't believe the old wives' tale 'Feed a cold' – that will just make you fat. You should try and rest more.

     a. 1 point   *b.* 0

16   If you suffer from an allergy and have recognised the causes and cures, then you are in total harmony with your body.

     Yes - 1 point   Don't suffer - 1 point

17   Exercise is essential to a healthy body and a conscious effort shows that you care about your health.

     Yes - 1 point   No - 0

18   If you find it easy to relax, which many people do not, then you are completely in tune.

     Yes - 1 point   No - 0

The Analysis

If you scored 16 - 18 then you are completely in tune with your body and its needs, and are probably in very good health.

If you scored 10 - 15 you care about your body, but perhaps don't look after it as much as you should.

If you scored 5 - 9 you take very little care of your body and are not in harmony with it. Your body should influence your lifestyle, not the other way about.

If you scored 0 - 4 you must be a physical wreck, it's a wonder you can stand upright. You should pay more attention to your body if it is to serve you properly.

35   IS A DIET WORTH WHILE ?

The Test

'Women, melons and cheese should be chosen by weight,' so say the Spaniards. In this country many people, and not only women, are obsessed with their figures and fear to be considered obese.

Some people on the other hand are simply plump and know losing weight would be such a painful discipline, they prefer not to contemplate it.

1   Stand naked in front of a mirror. Do you like what you see?
    a. Yes *b*. No *c*. In parts

2   Can you feel your ribs with ease?
    a. Yes *b*. No *c*. Only with effort

3   How many inches of fat can you pinch around your midriff?
    a. Less than one inch
    b. At least one inch
    c. Nearer six inches

4   Do you see a spare tyre around your middle?
    a. No *b*. A small one *c*. Yes

5   Try and touch your toes. Can you:
    a. Do it with ease?
    b. Only reach as far as your ankles?
    c. Only reach as far as your knees?

6   Run on the spot for one minute, raising your knees *at least* up to waist level as you do so. Do you feel:

a. Ready to carry on?
b. Slightly breathless?
c. Very breathless?

8 Plant your feet firmly on the ground and wriggle about. Is your body:
a. Very firm?
b. Slightly wobbly?
c. Reminiscent of a jelly?

9 Can you fit into clothes that you bought eighteen months ago?
a. With ease *b*. With a squeeze *c*. No

10 Do you feel embarrassed about your figure?
a. Never *b*. Sometimes *c*. All the time

The Analysis

Give yourself 2 points for each 'b' answer, and 3 points for every 'c' answer.

28 - 30 You are obese – there's no other word for it. It is bad for your health but it is not too late to diet. A crash diet is no good – see your doctor about a special diet for you.

20 - 26 It's no use mincing words – you're overweight. You have resigned yourself to being fat, or have not persevered with diets. A course at a weight-watchers' club would probably help.

8 - 18 You have a little excess fat in one or two areas, but are certainly not grossly overweight. But as this excess weight could put an extra strain on your heart, it might be an idea to cut out sugar, eat fewer carbohydrates, and try and get more exercise.

6 or less You have no real weight problem and should not contemplate a diet. You still need to exercise to keep fit, but basically you are in excellent shape.

36 ARE YOU ON THE VERGE OF A NERVOUS BREAKDOWN ?

The Test

A high proportion of the population spend at least some part of their lives in a mental hospital, take valium to calm them down, or suffer from a nervous disorder of some kind.

It is nothing to be ashamed of, but it would be better to avoid it altogether. Once you know the signs, that's the time to get professional help.

1 Do you ever feel really down and that life has little to offer you?
a. Often *b*. Occasionally *c*. Never

2 Do you take any kind of drug to calm you down?
a. Yes *b*. Occasionally *c*. Never

3 Do you ever resort to alcohol to 'steady your nerves'?
a. Daily *b*. Occasionally *c*. Never

4 Do you ever feel wound up to screaming pitch?
a. All the time *b*. On odd occasions *c*. Never

5 Do you find it impossible to relax?
a. Yes *b*. Sometimes *c*. No

6 Do you ever burst into tears?
a. Often *b*. Occasionally *c*. Never

7   Do you lie awake at nights worrying about a particular problem?
    a. Yes *b*. Sometimes *c*. Never

8   Do you find making yourself look smart and clean an effort?
    a. Always *b*. Sometimes *c*. Never

9   Do you get irritable and lose your temper easily?
    a. Yes *b*. Sometimes *c*. Never

10   Have you ever contemplated suicide?
    a. Often *b*. Once *c*. Never

11   Do you ever feel like running away from everything?
    a. Yes *b*. Only occasionally *c*. Never

12   Do you feel isolated and alone?
    a. Yes, all the time *b*. Occasionally *c*. Never

The Analysis

Give yourself 3 points for each 'a' answer and 2 points for every 'b' answer.

30 - 36   You have severe problems and there is a great strain on your nerves. Drugs and alcohol are not the answer and will create more problems than they will solve. You should seek professional advice to help you with your problems.

20 - 28   Your nerves are frayed at the edges and there is a danger of a nervous breakdown if you continue in the same way. Talk about your problems and get them out of your system. A lot of your trouble is psychological and talking to someone will help.

8 - 18   You are not on the verge of a breakdown . . . yet. There are, however, emotional strains in your life and you are subject to occasional depression. Talk to a friend about things that trouble you, go out and get yourself something to wear, go to a party, and cheer up.

6 or less   You have the average number of problems and know how to cope with them. Most of us feel low sometimes, and you are no exception. If you knew how to stay on top of the world all the time, we'd all want to know the secret.

37   ARE YOU LIKELY TO HAVE A HEART ATTACK ?

The Test

Coronary thrombosis is one of the major causes of death in this country. Heart disease can be accelerated by many things, and there are ways to cut down the risks.

How likely are you to suffer a heart attack, and is it too late to prevent it? Find out . . .

1   Do you smoke?
   a. Heavily *b.* Moderately *c.* Not at all

2   Do you do a lot of heavy lifting?
   a. Yes *b.* No more than most *c.* Very little if any

3   Do you consciously exercise your body?
   a. A daily routine
   b. At least once a week
   c. Never

4 Do you worry a lot about your job?
   a. Yes
   b. Sometimes
   c. No more than necessary or possible

5 Are you overweight?
   a. Yes, grossly *b.* Slightly *c.* No

6 Do you have infrequent bursts of energy when you move furniture around, or shovel snow?
   a. Yes, occasionally
   b. Once or twice a year
   c. I try to avoid sudden strenuous work

7 Do you consume vast quantities of sugar?
   a. Less than ten spoonfuls a day
   b. More than ten spoonfuls a day
   c. I don't take sugar

8 Do you get breathless walking upstairs?
   a. Frequently *b.* Occasionally *c.* Never

9 Do you ever get a pain that you take to be indigestion?
   a. Often *b.* Occasionally *c.* Never

10 Are you a big eater with a 'healthy' appetite?
   a. Yes *b.* Moderate eater *c.* Average eater

11 Do you ever find that sex is too strenuous for you and feel exhausted afterwards?
   a. Yes *b.* Occasionally *c.* No more than I ever did

12 Do you drink alcohol?
   a. Less than 2 pints of beer daily (or equivalent in alcoholic intake)
   b. More than 2 pints of beer daily
   c. Only the occasional drink

The Analysis

Give yourself 10 points for each answer that agrees with the following:

1   c   You should not smoke at all. Smoking causes a high percentage of heart attacks and deaths every year. It is never too late to give it up, and as well as making you a social outcast it can cause a lot of other serious illness, so STOP!

2   c   Heavy lifting is bad for you, especially if you are not used to it. If it is part of your job and you lift heavy weights daily, okay, but it does put a strain on your heart.

3   a   Ideally you should exercise daily. The Health Education Council can provide you with a simple daily routine that will keep you fit.

4   c   Worrying is bad for you and it is important to relax at the end of the day.

5   c   Again, excess weight puts a big strain on the heart. It will probably mean you have a high cholesterol level also which can lead to hardening of the arteries.

6   c   Sudden strenuous activity can be a shock to the system and a strain on the heart muscles. This frequently happens when people have heart attacks when shovelling snow in the winter.

7   c   Believe it or not the human body can survive quite well without taking in any sugar at all. You can survive quite happily, if not better, without it.

8 If you get breathless it means you are overweight or have the beginnings of a heart condition. See your doctor.

9 c Any frequent pain in your chest may not be indigestion, but something more serious. If it happens fairly often, see your doctor.

10 c Overeating will result in your getting fat, and we all know what fat does. Several light meals a day will do you far more good than one heavy one.

11 c It is natural to feel tired and ready for sleep after sex – that's normal, but if you feel breathless, completely drained, or in pain, something is wrong with the state of your body.

12 c The occasional drink now and again, even one sherry a day, can actually do you good. It is a good stimulant and a tonic, especially for old people. Like all things, however, excess is bad for you, and really heavy drinkers are just asking for a heart attack.

100 - 120 You are not likely to have a heart attack. Look after your well-being and your body will serve you well. A long life for you.

50 - 90 You are not respecting your heart as well as you might, and although a heart attack is not imminent you should take a little more care, especially with your diet.

10 - 40 There is a high risk that you will one day have a heart attack, and if you don't do something about it now, your days are numbered. Cut out

drinks and cigarettes, watch your food intake, and exercise more regularly. Take the dog for an extra long walk in the evening.

0   You could start digging your grave now – but you might drop dead before you finished. A thorough check up with your doctor is called for. Also see above.

38   ARE YOU YOUNG AT HEART ?

The Test

'Youth is the time to go flashing from one end of the world to the other, both in mind and body.'

ROBERT LOUIS STEVENSON (1881)

You've heard people say that you're as old as you feel and that old age is only a state of mind. You can have an old head on young shoulders – and vice versa. If you're young at heart you'll retain the joy of living always.

1   Do you think that face-lifts are foolish and that people should accept old age gracefully?

2   Is it unwise for a woman to marry a man younger than herself?

3   Do you think women should allow their hair to retain its natural colour, even if it is grey?

4   Do you think it is ridiculous for people over seventy to have an active sex life?

5   Is it too late at sixty-five to start learning a new skill?

6   Do you think it is a good thing that people are more open about their intimate relationships?

7   Would you regard a senior citizen as silly for wanting to wear fashionable clothes?

8   Do you enjoy surprises?

9   Do you enjoy going out in the evening and socialising?

10 Do you feel that you know all about life?

11 Do you remain in your present job because you think you're too old to change?

12 Do you feel guilty if you don't take things as seriously as you should?

13 Do you think it foolish of a mature woman to want to wear a wig or make-up to improve her looks?

14 Would you think an old person was ridiculous if they went on a diet to improve their figure?

15 Do you think that you are past taking up a new sport?

16 Would you try and forget it if you felt like doing something new and daring because people would think you were making a fool of yourself?

The Analysis

Give yourself 10 points for each question as follows:
1 - 7   NO   9 and 10   YES   11 - 16   NO

130 - 160	You are certainly young at heart, and believe that you are never too old to do anything you really want to. You're as old as you feel and you always feel young.
80 - 120	You are youthful in outlook and hate the thought of getting old. There are certain things, however, that you draw the line at because you do not wish to make a fool of yourself, or feel that you are not physically capable of.
30 - 70	There's still a flame burning brightly in your heart, and you try to remain youthful. However, you have limits, and believe that when you reach a certain age, there are some things one should forego. You would not wish to be accused of being 'mutton dressed as lamb' so keep to 'safe' clothes.
0 - 20	You are old before your time. Life has progressed, leaving you behind. It's not too late to catch up.

39   WILL YOU LIVE TO BE 100 ?

The Test

Try this test to find out what your chances are – and what you can do to improve them. First, look at the chart (on page 114) to find the average life expectancy for your age group and sex.

Then there are two sets of questions. They'll tell you what plus factors will increase the chance that you'll live to collect your pension and the minus ones which will reduce your prospects of enjoying it. There is still time to cheat the odds, although you may not be able to do anything about some factors – but others are within your control, and are yours to choose.

The Plus Factors

If you were offered a guarantee that you'd live to be
100 you'd be delighted   + 2

You take life fairly calmly, it takes a lot to provoke
you   + 3

You enjoy regular sex with your regular partner
once or twice a week   + 2

You are a light drinker – once in a while but not
every day   + 1½

You drink daily, on average, a couple of tots of
spirits, or half a litre of wine or four glasses of beer+ 3

You prefer simple plain foods like vegetables and
fruits rather than richer, fattier ones   + ½

You almost never leave the meal table feeling full   + ½

Your job is professional   + 1½

Your job is one involving technical skills or you are in
management or administration or work on the land+ 1

Your job is not labouring, but does keep you physically active, as well as mentally   + 2

You live, or have mostly lived, in the country   + 1

You are married and live with your husband or wife + 1

You are above average intelligence + 2

You have at least one close friend and can confide anything that is worrying you + 1

One or more of your grandparents lived to be 80 or more. For each one who did + 1

Your mother lived to be 80 or more + 4

Your father topped 80 + 2

You have a thorough medical check-up every second year if you are male, and once a year, including a cancer smear, if you are female

You exercise energetically three times a week + 3

You went to university and did post-graduate work there + 3

You got an ordinary degree + 2

You have at least one 'A' level + 1

You are 65 or over and still at work + 3

You are 60 and still at work + 2

You already have at least one hobby or interest that you are looking forward to having more time for when you retire + 1

You have walked up a mountain or done something
equally strenuous in the last eighteen months   + 1

You don't go in for dangerous sports   + 1

The Minus Factors

You drink heavily – more than a couple of tots of
spirits, half a litre of wine or four glasses of beer
every day   – 8

You often feel like a human volcano – ready to blow
your top at any minute   – 2

You rarely or never do up your seat belt   – 1

You have three or more offences for speeding or
know that it's just a matter of luck that you haven't   – 1

You keep yourself to yourself – you're too busy to get
involved in other people's lives   – 3½

You hate change   – 2

You love change so much you're always doing it –
your job, marriage partner, home   – 2

You live in a city or large town   – 1

Your job is semi-skilled   – ½

Your job is labouring   – 4

You have been worried or depressed a lot of the time
during the last two years   – 2

You are ill often   − 5

You have a chronic illness like migraine or bronchial
trouble   − 5

You are more hard up than most of your family,
friends and neighbours   − 1

At work, you sit down most of the time   − 2

You sleep more than ten or less than five hours a night − 2

If any of your brothers, sisters, parents or grandparents died:
    Of a heart complaint or stroke before 50, for each
    one   − 4
    Between 50 and 60 of either, for each   − 2
    Of diabetes or an ulcer before they were 60, for
    each   − 3
    Of a stomach cancer before they were 60, for each − 2
    Of any illness (not accident) before 60, for each   − 1

If you are a childless woman who cannot or plans
not to have children   − 1

If you are a woman with more than seven children− 1

If you smoke in a day: less than twenty cigarettes − 2
                      twenty - forty   − 7
                      more than forty   − 12

If you are up to three kilos overweight:
    men 20 - 25   − 11
         25 - 30   − 8
         30 - 35   − 5
         35 - 40   − 3½
         40 - 50   − 2½

women 20 - 30	− 5½
30 - 45	− 5
45 - 55	− 3½

If you are more than three kilos overweight, in addition   − 2

If you have been overweight in the past   − 2

If you are divorced or separated:
men living alone	− 7
men living with others	− 3½
women living alone	− 4
women living with others	− 2

If you are a widow living alone   − 3½

If you are a widow living with others   − 2

If you are a widower living alone   − 7

If you are a widower living with others   − 3½

If you are an unmarried woman (with or without a live-in lover), for every ten years since 25   − 1

If you are a bachelor, sharing living quarters for every year you've clocked up another decade past your 25th birthday   − 1

THIS IS YOUR LIFE EXPECTANCY

The first column is your present age. The one to the right of it is the age a man of that age can expect to reach and the next one across is the average female life expectancy at that age.

Age Now	Male	Female	Age Now	Male	Female	Age Now	Male	Female
15	70.7	73.7	42	72.7	75.7	69	79.7	82.7
16	70.8	73.8	43	72.8	75.8	70	80.2	83.2
17	70.8	73.8	44	72.9	75.9	71	80.7	83.7
18	70.9	73.9	45	73.0	76.0	72	81.2	84.2
19	71.0	73.0	46	73.2	76.2	73	81.7	84.7
20	71.1	73.1	47	73.3	76.3	74	82.2	85.2
21	71.1	73.1	48	73.5	76.5	75	82.8	85.8
22	71.2	74.2	49	73.6	76.6	76	83.3	86.3
23	71.3	74.3	50	73.8	76.8	77	83.9	86.9
24	71.3	74.3	51	74.0	77.0	78	84.5	87.5
25	71.4	74.4	52	74.2	77.2	79	85.1	88.1
26	71.5	74.5	53	74.4	77.4	80	85.7	88.7
27	71.6	74.6	54	74.7	77.7			
28	71.6	74.6	55	74.9	77.9			
29	71.7	74.7	56	75.1	78.1			
30	71.8	74.8	57	75.4	78.4			
31	71.9	74.9	58	75.7	78.7			
32	71.9	74.9	59	76.0	79.0			
33	72.0	75.0	60	76.3	79.3			
34	72.0	75.0	61	76.6	79.6			
35	72.1	75.1	62	77.0	80.0			
36	72.2	75.2	63	77.3	80.3			
37	72.2	75.2	64	77.7	80.7			
38	72.3	75.3	65	78.1	81.1			
39	72.4	75.4	66	78.4	81.4			
40	72.5	75.5	67	78.9	81.9			
41	72.6	75.6	68	79.3	82.3			

The Analysis

Well, now you know the worst, it's up to you to do what you can to make it better.

And there is more at stake than the years shown in the chart – the test tells you the state of play today. It doesn't take into account research that is currently being done which could provide cures for existing diseases.

What this means is the more you can extend your own life span, the more likely you are to be around to cash in on any bonuses they are handing out from the research laboratories.

40 DOES YOUR SPEECH LET YOU DOWN ?

The Test

An old Japanese proverb says 'The tongue should be feared more than the sword' – your speech can be very revealing and expose your true self.

How you speak can put you under fierce attack, and whoever claimed 'words can never hurt me' was probably stone deaf, because we are judged by our speech – ill-mannered speaking generally suggests an uncouth person.

What does your speech say about you?

1   Do you have a strong accent that embarrasses you?

2   Do you enjoy listening to your voice on tape?

3   Do you make a conscious effort to speak nicely?

4   Would you say that you are articulate?

5   Do you interrupt people when they are talking?

6   Do people ever complain that your voice is loud?

7   Do you attempt to make sure that your sentences are grammatically correct?

8   Do you use colloquial expressions which people from other parts of the country may not understand?

9   Do you drop your 'h's' and say 'ouse, 'andsome, or 'ospital?

10 Do you ever mumble?

11 Do you drop your voice at the end of sentences?

12 Does your voice go high when you are nervous?

13 Do you find it easy to speak words of comfort and reassurance?

14 Do you ever find people using long words that you do not understand?

15 Do you ever use words of which you do not fully understand the meaning?

16 Do you try and speak more clearly on the telephone?

17 Do you ever try and adopt a 'posh' accent so as not to feel inferior?

18 Do you try and make lots of witty comments?

19 Do you get morbid and talk about depressing things when you feel down?

20 Do you find yourself speaking extra fast when you are excited?

The Analysis

Give yourself 5 points for each answer that agrees with the following.

1. NO	2. YES	3. YES	4. YES	5. NO
6. NO	7. YES	8. NO	9. NO	10. NO
11. NO	12. NO	13. YES	14. NO	15. NO
16. YES	17. NO	18. NO	19. NO	20. NO

80 - 100 You are very articulate and conscious of the way you speak. You have been educated to speak nicely and enjoy listening to others who have good voices. It must be pleasant to hold a conversation with you.

55 - 75 Your voice is not as good as it might be. You know how to speak properly, but it is easy for you to get into sloppy speaking habits, especially when with people whose speech pattern is not as good as yours.

25 - 50 Your speech is poor and can let you down at times. You may find yourself repeating sentences in order to make your meaning clear. Slow your speech down slightly, be more aware of lips, teeth and tongue and the role they play.

20 or less You really should have elocution lessons. You have a careless way of speaking, possibly because of the region in which you were brought up. There is nothing wrong with having an accent, but it helps if people can understand what you are saying. Make a tape recording of your voice and listen to it critically.

41 ARE YOU AN INTELLECTUAL?

The Test

Do you consider that you have a high degree of intellect and a supply of knowledge stored in your head? Or are you on the same level as Winnie the Pooh who said: 'I am a Bear of Very Little Brain and long words Bother me.'?

The following test will see how intelligent you are and your powers of intellect will be called for.

1   What do the following phrases mean?
    a. *non omnis moriari*
    b. *Sic transit gloria mundi*
    c. *ad hoc*
    d. *modus operandi*
    e. *avant garde*

2   Which of Shakespeare's sonnets contains this couplet?
    'All days are nights to see till I see thee,
    And nights bright days when dreams do show thee me.'

3   Who wrote the immortal words:
    'They shall grow not old, as we that are left grow old,
    Age shall not weary them, nor the years condemn.'?

4   No man is good, but some men are not bad. Therefore,
    a. All men are not bad
    b. All men aren't good
    c. No man is not bad

5   Which number is wrong in this series?
    1, 19, 8, 5, 145, 127

6   Who said: 'Fasten your seatbelts, it's going to be a
    bumpy ride.'?
    a. Mae West
    b. Bette Davis
    c. Bette Midler

7   Who painted the picture entitled 'And when did you
    last see your father?'
    a. W. F. Yeames
    b. Sir Edward Landseer
    c. Vermeer

8   Who was Henry VII's mother?
    a. Eleanor of Castille
    b. Eleanor of Acquitaine
    c. Margaret Beaufort

9   What was the relationship of King George VI to the
    present Earl of St Andrews?
    a. Great Uncle
    b. Great Grandfather
    c. Grandfather

10 What are the principal ingredients of the iced cocktail
    daiquiri?
    a. Vermouth and orange juice
    b. Cuban rum, lime juice and sugar
    c. White rum and lemon juice, brown sugar

11   Which statements are true?
     a. The gestation period of a rhinoceros is 365 days
     b. The African elephant always sleeps standing up, which means that it is on its feet for fifty years
     c. 7½ million tonnes of water evaporate from the Dead Sea every day

12   One bunch of bananas has one-third again as many bananas as a second bunch. If the second bunch has three fewer bananas than the first bunch, how many has the first bunch?

The Analysis

Give yourself ONE point for each correct answer:

1   a. I leave something for posterity
    b. Thus passes the glory of the world
    c. Impromptu
    d. Method of operation
    e. Ahead of one's time

2   XLIII   3   Lawrence Binyon   4   b

5   8   6   Bette Davis in 'All About Eve'

7   W. F. Yeames   8   c   9   a

10   b   11   a. False. The gestation period is 560 days
                    b. True
                    c. True

12   The first bunch has twelve bananas

Total – 18 points

120

16 - 18	You are indeed an intellectual and should enter for 'Mastermind'.

12 - 15	Not bad. You have the makings of an intellectual, but are not quite articulate enough to hold your own in conversation.

Less than 12	You may be bright, but nowhere near dazzling enough to be considered brainbox of the year. Sorry.

42   IS YOUR MIND OFTEN ON OTHER THINGS ?

The Test

Are you so preoccupied with your own life that you cannot see the wood for the trees? Are you fully aware of what is going on in the world, or are you only concerned with what goes on inside your own boundary?

1   Does a colleague or friend ever say anything to you about 'the rail strike' or 'the recession' – an event of which you know nothing?
   a. Often *b*. Sometimes *c*. Never

2   Do you ever get ready to go out, not realising that it is pouring with rain?
   a. Often *b*. Sometimes *c*. Never

3   Have you ever woken up in the morning and for a few moments had no idea what day of the week it was?
   a. Frequently *b*. Occasionally *c*. Never

4　Does your spouse or partner ever talk to you for some minutes and accuse you of being 'miles away'?
　　a. Often *b*. Sometimes *c*. Never

5　Have you ever missed your stop on a train or bus because you were deep in thought?
　　a. Often *b*. Sometimes *c*. Never

6　Do you know what the headlines are on today's news-paper? (without looking before you answer)
　　a. Yes *b*. No

7　Do you take any notice of events, such as Mother's Day or Father's Day?
　　a. Always *b*. Never

8　Do you miss your lunch break at work?
　　a. At least once a week
　　b. At least once a month
　　c. Never

9　Does the news of a friend's divorce ever come as a complete surprise to you?
　　a. Occasionally *b*. Never

10　Are there many little jobs around the house that would take only a short time to do, but never seem to get done?
　　a. Lots
　　b. A few
　　c. None – I see to them straight away

The Analysis

1. a - 3   2. a - 3   3. a - 3   4. a - 3
    b - 2   b - 2   b - 2   b - 2

5. a - 3   6. b - 3   7. b - 3   8. a - 3
    b - 2   b - 2

9. a - 3   10. a - 3
                   b - 2

21 - 30   You aren't informed at all and must be very frustrating to your friends and family because you've continually got your mind on other things. You really need to take more interest in people and events apart from those that impinge on your own world.

14 - 20   You are probably known as a scatterbrain or considered to be a little eccentric. It is all right if you concentrate on one thing at a time. but this often leads to the exclusion of important things.

Less than 13   You seem to know exactly what you are doing. You care about other people and their lives and the events of the world. You can be trusted not to let people down.

43 DOES YOUR MEMORY LET YOU DOWN ?

The Test

How good is your memory? Do you have the name of some-one on the tip of your tongue, but are unable to spit it out? Do you have total recall and a photographic mind? Few people are so fortunate, but is your memory as good as you think it is?

1 How good are you at remembering your wife's/ husband's birthday?
   a. Never forget
   b. Always remember it just in time
   c. Sometimes forget it completely

2 Do you ever meet someone in the street and remember the face but not the name?
   a. Frequently *b*. Occasionally *c*. Never

3 Have you ever gone into a room to look for something and forgotten what it is you went in for?
   a. Often *b*. Sometimes *c*. Never

4 Do your family or friends ever try and remind you of something they told you the previous day and you feel positive that they did not?
   a. Almost daily *b*. On rare occasions *c*. Never

5 Do you ever forget your own telephone number?
   a. Often *b*. Sometimes *c*. Never

6 How many names can you remember of children that you were with in your first class at primary school?
   a. At least six *b*. More than six *c*. None

7   Do you always know what the date is?
    a. Never remember
    b. Usually know within a day or two
    c. Always remember the exact date

8   Do you ever hum a song to yourself but can't remember
    the words or the title?
    a. Frequently *b.* Occasionally *c.* Always remember

9   Could you remember, if necessary, all the presents you
    received for Christmas a year ago, and who they were
    from?
    a. Yes, most of them
    b. Only those from close members of the family
    c. Can't even remember Christmas a year ago

10 Look at the following words for *one minute*. Then close
    the book and see how many of the words you can write
    down:

ULTIMATE FINANCIAL INTERREGNUM OUST
PARADOX LINEN INFLATE HIS DISSUADE
JEALOUS KIBBUTZ WALRUS OSCAR MOON
PLOUGH SIMPLE THEM RECITATION MAN

The Analysis

1. a - 3	2. c - 3	3. c - 3	4. c - 3
b - 1	b - 1	b - 1	b - 1

5. c - 3	6. b - 3	7. c - 3	8. c - 3
b - 1	a - 1	b - 1	b - 1

9. a - 3
    b - 1

10. 15-19 words - 5   12-14 words - 4
    9-11 words - 3   6- 8 words - 2
    Less than 6 words - 1

30 - 32   You have an excellent memory which rarely lets you down. Your photographic mind enables you to recall many events that other people have long since forgotten.

21 - 29   You have a good memory and usually remember anything important. Occasionally you forget minor things, probably because your mind was preoccupied with other activities.

11 - 20   You will be the first to admit that your memory is not infallible, and can be an embarrassment for you at times. Fortunately you remember things important to you, but may upset others by your oversights.

Less than 11 It's a wonder you remember to get up in the morning.

44   ARE YOU IN GOOD HEALTH ?

The Test

How healthy are you? Are you of above average fitness, or do you suffer from niggling aches and pains that you try to ignore?

1   If you run up a flight of steps do you get breathless?
    a. Very *b*. Slightly *c*. Not at all

2   Try and touch your toes *now*. How far could you reach?
    a. To your toes easily
    b. As far as your ankles
    c. Only as far as your knees

3   How often do you suffer from colds?
     a. On average one per winter
     b. No more than three per year
     c. Three or more a year

4   If you carry something very heavy do you have aching
     muscles the next day?
     a. Sometimes *b*. Always *c*. Never

5   Are you actively involved in any kind of sport?
     a. Weekly *b*. Occasionally *c*. Never

6   Do you go to sleep within half an hour of going to bed?
     a. Every night *b*. Most nights *c*. Never

7   Do you wake in the mornings feeling full of energy and
     ready to face the world?
     a. Always *b*. Sometimes *c*. Never

8   Do you suffer from headaches?
     a. Frequently *b*. Occasionally *c*. Never

9   How often do you feel irritable or touchy?
     a. Frequently *b*. Occasionally *c*. Rarely

10   In what condition are your hair and nails?
     a. Glossy and strong *b*. Dry and brittle

11   Do you consciously exercise?
     a. Daily *b*. Weekly *c*. Never

12   Do you watch your calorie intake?
     a. Always *b*. Never

The Analysis

Give yourself 3 for each of the following:

1. c	2. a	3. a	4. c
5. a	6. a	7. a	8. c
9. c	10. a	11. a	12. a

30-36   You are in peak condition and should have no worries about your health.

18-29   You are in good condition but are inclined to be overweight and probably eat the wrong kind of foods.

Under 18 You are below par and should take more care of your body, especially if you want to be fit in later life.

<u>45   ARE YOU A HYPOCHONDRIAC ?</u>

The Test

Do you suffer from psychological illnesses? You may not think you do, but to the hypochondriac a real physical pain can be all in the mind . . .

Answer YES or NO to the following questions:

1   Do you enjoy the fuss, attention and being pampered when you are ill?

2   If you go away for a weekend break do you take more than a bottle of aspirins with you in case you are ill?

3   If someone at work has a streaming cold do you try and avoid them, and hold your breath if they come near?

4   Do you ever get a slight sniffle that seems to hang on for days, and are convinced that it is going to turn into 'flu?

5   Suddenly one evening you sneeze a couple of times for no apparent reason, do you immediately dash to the medicine cabinet to try and prevent a cold?

6   If you hear or read about a particular illness, do you feel convinced you have the same symptoms?

7   Do you ever worry at night that you may have some serious illness, like cancer or multiple sclerosis?

8   Do you worry about the cleanliness of your body and your home?

9   If you heard that someone had died of food poisoning from eating a particular product, would you avoid that product in future?

10   Do you visit your doctor more than six times a year?

11   If you see a new medical product advertised do you buy some just in case it might be needed?

12   Do you ever get depressed about your body and health?

13   Do you make unnecessary appointments with dentists or opticians?

14   Within the last month have you suspected that you have had something wrong with you and it has turned out to be unfounded?

The Analysis

Give yourself one point for every YES answer.

12 - 14   You are obsessed with your health and are suffering from acute hypochondria. You must learn to relax or it could seriously damage your health (but don't take pills to help you to relax).

8 - 11   You are verging on being a hypochondriac. Looking after your health is one thing, but imaginary complaints are another – and you have more than your fair share of psychological ailments.

3 - 7   You are cautious about your health and don't enjoy being ill. You take sensible precautions believing that prevention is better than cure.

Under 3   You are not a hypochondriac, and probably enjoy very good health. You try to shrug off illness, will not take to your bed unless forced, and only visit the doctor if you have good cause to worry.

46   ARE YOU A POTENTIAL MURDERER ?

The Test

'We kill everybody, my dear. Some with bullets, some with words, and everybody with our deeds. We drive people into their graves, and neither see it nor feel it.'

MAXIM GORKY 'Enemies'

130

Are you a potential murderer? Do you have the capacity to kill someone? What drives people to murder, and could you be tipped over the edge? Find out . . .

1 Do you go through periods when you feel deeply depressed?
   a. Sometimes *b*. Often *c*. Never

2 Do you ever feel so frustrated that you could scream?
   a. Sometimes *b*. Often *c*. Never

3 Is there someone in your life who annoys you intensely?
   a. Yes
   b. Someone who makes me angry occasionally
   c. No-one

4 Do people's little habits and traits irritate you?
   a. Yes, always *b*. Occasionally *c*. Never

5 Do you ever have uncontrollable rages when you throw things around?
   a. Yes *b*. Only very rarely *c*. Never

6 Do you turn violent when severely provoked?
   a. Often *b*. Occasionally *c*. Never

7 Do you ever regret the life you lead and wish that you were in a better situation?
   a. All the time
   b. Only when I'm really down
   c. Never

8 Did you have a good relationship with your parents?
   a. Yes, very good
   b. We tolerated each other
   c. I hated the sight of them

9   Do you have relationship problems and find it difficult to settle down?
    a. Yes *b.* No

10 Do you ever have long periods of aggressiveness when you feel ill at ease with the world and are rude to everyone for no particular reason?
    a. Frequently *b.* Occasionally *c.* Never

11 Do you find it difficult to forgive people?
    a. Yes, very *b.* No, I forgive and forget

12 Have you ever felt it would be easy to kill someone, and in fact contemplated the results of such an action?
    a. Yes, frequently *b.* Occasionally *c.* Never

The Analysis

1.	a - 2	2.	a - 2	3.	a - 3	4.	a - 3
	b - 3		b - 3		b - 2		b - 2
5.	a - 3	6.	a - 3	7.	a - 3	8.	b - 2
	b - 2		b - 2		b - 2		c - 3
9.	a - 3	10.	a - 3	11.	a - 3	12.	a - 3
			b - 2				b - 2

33 - 36 If you don't curb your feelings and passions you could turn into another Crippen, so take care. If you feel really depressed, you should seek professional help.

24 - 32 We all have the power and potential to commit murder, but you have a greater potential than most, although you have never seriously planned such a thing. It takes a lot to push you over the top but if you were really provoked, you could be a danger.

15 - 23 You sometimes get very frustrated and have some regrets. There may be someone in your life who you feel has held you back, but you have never seriously contemplated doing away with them.

14 or less Of course you are capable of murder, but you are less likely to commit such an action on the spur of the moment as the above. Yours would be a planned, calculated deed for personal gain only.

47   ARE YOU STIMULATING TO OTHERS ?

The Test

When we come in contact with a stimulating personality, it is like stepping from darkness into the sunshine.

How do such people do it? They obviously enjoy every minute of their lives. What makes them so interested and so interesting?

Answer yes or no to the following:

1   You are interested in a wide variety of things, as well as specially in one or two things.

2   You like trying out new ideas and new methods of doing things.

3   You are not afraid or self-conscious of being and sounding enthusiastic.

4   Within reason, you are ready and willing to drop what you are doing at the moment to take part in a surprise activity, like a drive or a picnic, or a shopping expedition.

5   You like all kinds of people and you like people as people, instead of hand-picking your friends because you share the same social background or work in the same office.

6   It is exciting to meet new people, attend social functions, be expected to take part.

7   Mistakes and failures do not depress you for long because there are so many other interesting things to do.

8   You are too interested in learning and too keen on doing things yourself to bother about pleasing everybody and being criticised.

9   You like asking questions and finding out the answers.

10 You are ready to take the initiative and lead the way.

11 You are willing to shoulder responsibility.

12 You can encourage the waverers and fainthearts.

13 You like seeing that everybody has a good time.

14 You always have plenty to talk about and you enjoy talking, especially friendly arguments and discussions.

15 Conversely, you equally enjoy listening to other people.

16 You like to have people calling casually on you, and make it obvious that they are welcome any time.

17   You find it easy to fit in and take pot luck.

18   You never mind looking silly when it is all in the cause of good fun.

19   You are extra quick off the mark with sympathy, congratulations, offers of help.

20   You believe that you still have a lot to learn, and know that you are learning something every day, especially about people.

The Analysis

Give yourself 5 points for every YES.

70 - 100   You are an outstandingly stimulating person with a keen interest outside yourself. You leave a place the brighter for having been there.

60 - 65   You have periods of being very stimulating but find it difficult to keep it up sometimes. Still, your company is nearly always welcome.

50 - 55   Only fair – your light is somewhat dim.

Less   Your light seems to have gone out. Time to relight the touchpaper.

48 HOW WELL DO YOU KNOW YOURSELF ?

The Test

We think we know ourselves well – but do we? Psychologists tell us we do not. We close our eyes not only to our faults, but to our strengths and virtues as well.

But if we are brave enough to take a fresh look at our real selves, it can be surprising and rewarding. So, if you dare, do this test and find out who you really are.

1 Which of these do you think is a more important quality for people to have:
   a. a sense of humour *b.* a strong character

2 Which of these lists contains more items in which you are interested:
   a. football, radio or model-building, climbing or camping?
   b. books, music, art?

3 If you had to do a test for a job you very much wanted would you be hoping for:
   a. questions with one right answer on which you would score if you got it correct?
   b. questions with no right answer on which you would be judged on your originality?

4 Which of these would you rather do:
   a. make a breakthrough in scientific research?
   b. make a great movie?

5 Which of these do you think is more important in bringing up children:

a. teaching them to cope with the practical demands of life?

b. teaching them to think for themselves?

6 Would you prefer to wallpaper your bedroom with:
   a. a pretty, small floral pattern?
   b. a geometric design?
   c. stripes?

7 If you could take the trans-Siberian railway, would you set out anticipating:
   a. adventure, perhaps even romance?
   b. endless boredom?
   c. an interesting experience?

8 If you shared a compartment with strangers on a long train journey would you be likely to start a conversation?
   a. yes
   b. no
   c. no, but would join in if someone else started it

9 Which of these best describes your attitude to people you meet for the first time:
   a. You expect to like them until they do or say something to change your mind?
   b. You are polite but reserved until you have had time to size them up?
   c. You try to behave as if you liked them, but really reserve judgement until you know them better?

10 If you are in unfamiliar surroundings, would you hide your money before you went to sleep at night:
   a. Only if you had been specially warned you were in a high risk area?
   b. As a matter of course?
   c. Perhaps, if you thought of it?

11 Which of these holidays would most appeal to you?
    a. You, or you and your partner alone on a tropical island
    b. A villa or apartment in a beauty spot undiscovered by tourists
    c. A lively resort with bustling streets and plenty of night life

12 If you were stranded alone on an island for a week would you be most pleased to get away from?
    a. people
    b. traffic and telephones
    c. nothing. Even a week would be too long

13 Do you regard spending an evening alone as:
    a. a luxury?
    b. a chance to catch up on things you haven't been able to get around to?
    c. a disaster to be avoided?

14 Would you rather be able to:
    a. write a great book?
    b. be competent at everything you do?
    c. play with a great orchestra?

15 How do you most enjoy your favourite music?
    a. playing a good recording on first class equipment
    b. listening with friends
    c. in a concert audience

16 If you were invited to make a speech would you:
    a. quite enjoy it?
    b. not look forward to it but know deep down you would be alright once you started?
    c. Refuse? You just could not do it?

17 Do you arrive at parties:
  a. anticipating pleasantly the evening ahead?
  b. excited and a little nervous at the prospect?
  c. full of dread?

18 If you saw someone looking unwell on a train or bus would you:
  a. ask them if they feel ill?
  b. say nothing, but keep an eye on them?
  c. get the urge to get off at the next stop in case you get involved?

19 If someone you have just met pays you a compliment do you:
  a. thank them gracefully?
  b. think of something sparkling you should have said when you get into bed that night?
  c. blush, break out in a sweat, and/or lose the power of speech?

20 Trapped in a corner with a bore, do you:
  a. escape, even if you have to be brutal?
  b. put your mind to work on how to slide out without being rude?
  c. console yourself it is better than being ignored altogether?

The Analysis

If your answers consisted mainly of 'a' choices, you are one of those people who can go straight to the heart of a problem and find a sensible solution to it. You are idealistic about life and people. You always expect the best and even when disappointed this does not shake your basic optimism. You can take pleasure in solitary pursuits, and are very self-reliant.

If your answers consisted mainly of 'b' choices, you are more creative than practical. You do not go for obvious solutions for problems. But you are realistic about people and situations. You do not have wild expectations and take life, warts and all. You can tolerate your own company quite well but are fairly confident socially.

Mainly 'c' answers indicate you have a balanced outlook, sensibly wary but can be pleasantly surprised – you do not always expect the worst. Shyness is a problem with you and perhaps you do not think highly enough of yourself. You are happiest in the company of family and old friends.

49   HOW WELL DO YOU KNOW YOUR PARENTS ?

The Test

We all think we know our parents well – we've known them all our lives. But that woman you've lived with has usually just been your 'mother' and not a real human being.

Can you imagine your mother as a child? Can you imagine your parents having a sexual relationship? So often parents are taken for granted, and not appreciated until they are gone.

Answer the following questions, then get your parents, if possible, to check the answers.

1   My MOTHER was born in .... (Town)

2   My FATHER was born in .... (Town)

3   My MOTHER is .... years old

4   My FATHER is .... years old

5   When my parents were children their ambitions were:

Mother ....

Father ....

6   Did your Mother/Father have nicknames at school and what were they?

7   Where did your parents first meet?

8   Who were your Mother's/Father's first boyfriend/girlfriend?

9   What were your Mother's/Father's best subject(s) at school?

10 What is your Mother's greatest fear?

11 When did your father propose to your mother?

12 Where were your mother and father married and in which year?

13 What was the first gift your father gave your mother?

14 What is your mother's favourite colour?

15 What was your father's favourite sport at school?

16 What causes the most arguments between your parents?

17 What is your MOTHER's favourite food?

18 What is your FATHER's favourite food?

19 Given the choice of a car which would your father choose:
a. Mercedes *b*. Renault *c*. Datsun *d*. Ford

20 Given the choice of holidays, which would your mother choose:
a. Switzerland?
b. America?
c. Spain?
d. Within the British Isles?

21 What is your MOTHER's favourite book?

22 Which is your FATHER's favourite film of all time?

23 If you decided to live with someone without marrying, would your parents object?

24 Do you know how your parents vote?

25 What kind of music does your MOTHER most enjoy?

26 What kind of music does your FATHER most enjoy:
a. Popular?
b. Classical?
c. Jazz?
d. Country and Western?
e. Folk?

27 Given the choice of the following venues, which would your mother choose for an evening out:
a. Cinema?
b. Theatre?
c. Candlelit restaurant?
d. Dance hall?

28   Does your FATHER have a strong religious feeling?

29   Does your MOTHER have any allergies?

30   What hobbies would your parents take up, given the chance?

The Analysis

Give yourself 10 points for each answer that your parents agree on. Highest score 340.

290 - 340   You know your parents very well and must be exceptionally close. Your parents must be honest with you and open about themselves.

220 - 280   You know your parents quite well, but there are probably one or two episodes from their childhood that they haven't spoken to you about. On the whole you have a good relationship.

150 - 210   You don't know your parents as well as you might. It is probably their early life that they keep quiet about, perhaps because you haven't shown enough interest in them as people.

70 - 140   You treat your parents with respect, but expect them to be very supportive, acting as 'provider' and 'banker' rather than as a man and woman. Perhaps you should show just a little more interest in their feelings.

60 or less   Either you have never taken a great interest in your parents' lives or else they are very reserved. It could be that they have strict values, and find it embarrassing to discuss their lives with you.

Show them that you are now an adult, and as they give you the answers to these questions, you could discover a great deal more about them.

50 ARE YOU A TELEVISION ADDICT ?

The Test

A disease of present-day society is too much television, and it can happen to anyone. Do you study the *Radio* and *TV Times* from cover to cover and plan your week's viewing and centre your life around it?

Do you watch more than six hours television a week? You could well be on the way to becoming a TV addict.

1 Do you enjoy watching anything on television, or do you only switch it on for a programme you particularly want to see?
a. Will watch anything
b. Will only watch a programme if it interests me

2 If there are two programmes you want to watch one evening – one that ends at 7.30 pm and the second one beginning at 8.15 pm, would you watch the programme in between for forty-five minutes whilst you were waiting?
a. Yes *b.* No

3 If you were at a friend's house when a favourite programme was on would you:
a. ask if you could watch it?
b. forget about it for once?

4 If you were visiting someone and you knew that they only had a black-and-white set, would you prefer to stay home and watch a favourite programme in colour or would you put up with it in black-and-white?
   a. Stay and watch it in colour
   b. Watch in black-and-white

5 How many hours of television do you watch each week on average?
   a. More than six hours
   b. Less than six hours

6 Do you ever watch television right through to the Epilogue?
   a. Always or sometimes *b*. Never

7 Do you watch television with the light out or on?
   a. Out *b*. On

8 Do you have the television on if you are doing something else, eg ironing?
   a. Usually have it on *b*. Only have it on to watch

9 Do you ever write to or ring the TV companies to the times of your viewing, or do you automatically remember?
   a. I remember *b*. I have to check

10 Do you ever write to or ring the TV companies to complain about a programme?
   a. Sometimes *b*. Never

11 Do you have more than one television set in your house?
   a. Yes *b*. No

12   If your television goes wrong do you rent or borrow
     another one while it is being repaired?
     a. Yes *b.* No

The Analysis

For every question that you give an 'a' answer, give yourself
3 points.

30-36   You must have square eyes and allow that little
          box to dominate your life. You are a human TV
          guide and life could be passing you by.

18-27   You spend far too much time in front of your set
          and are prepared to watch anything. It is one of
          your major interests and you would feel lost with-
          out it, even though you do have other interests.

15 or   You have a sensible attitude to viewing. You know
under   what you like and are not prepared to watch any
          old thing. You could quite happily survive without
          it, but appreciate its educational and communi-
          cative value.

51   WHAT ARE YOUR SECRET TALENTS ?

The Test

Do you know what you are good at? Or are your hidden
abilities concealed even from yourself?

   Find our what talents you really have - and how to use
them.

1   Do you think love at first sight is:
    a. improbable, if not actually impossible?
    b. a polite name for lust at first sight?
    c. a premonition that this is the person you can share your secret thoughts with?

2   Which of these seduction techniques appeals most to you:
    a. fresh sheets, a warm bedroom, phone off the hook?
    b. an eager, if slightly nervous, partner?
    c. black satin sheets and an open window with a view of a full moon outside?

3   Are you happiest in: (*men only*)
    a. a good suit and tie?
    b. jeans and a T-shirt?
    c. a kaftan?

4   Are you happiest in: (*women only*)
    a. an expensive suit or tailored dress?
    b. an Indian peasant dress?
    c. a swirling summer 'garden party' dress and elegant sandals?

5   At school were you best at:
    a. mathematics or science?
    b. getting on with your classmates?
    c. literature or art?

6   Would you describe your parents as mainly:
    a. strict? *b.* loving? *c.* easy-going?

7   If you are window shopping and you see an evening dress/suit that knocks your eye out, do you ask yourself:

a. would it fit in with my existing wardrobe?

b. would he/she like me in it?

c. can I live without it?

8   Lying in the sun on a summer day would you be more likely to notice:

   a. the proportion of cloud to blue sky?

   b. how some of the cloud shapes look like animals or people?

   c. the patterns the clouds make against the sky?

9   Would you prefer to drive:

   a. a Rolls Royce?

   b. a Mercedes custom-converted to an estate?

   c. an E-type Jaguar?

10   Do you think arranged marriages:

   a. have a lot of advantages?

   b. could succeed - but it would take a lot of hard work?

   c. are to the victims like the cages are to caged birds?

11   Compared with your friends were you:

   a. an early developer? *b.* average? *c.* late?

12   Would a stroll through the countryside interest you more for:

   a. the bird species you might spot?

   b. the company?

   c. the beauty of the landscape?

13   If you were cast away on a desert island with just one of the following, which do you hope it would be:

   a. a computer and teach-yourself book of computing?

   b. an album of your favourite photographs?

   c. a piano?

14 Which of the following would you rather watch on television?
   a. a documentary on the background to a news story?
   b. a romantic old movie?
   c. a commentary on art in the 20th century?

15 Would you prefer to be given free tickets to:
   a. a classical concert?
   b. a Sinatra concert?
   c. a Rolling Stones concert?

16 Which colour do you like best?
   a. blue? *b.* yellow? *c.* red?

17 Which of these upsets you most:
   a. having a mess around you?
   b. having a row with someone you love?
   c. not being able to express something you want to say?

18 If you saw a bad car crash would you first:
   a. dial the emergency services?
   b. rush to see how seriously hurt the people in it were?
   c. get someone to do one while you did the other?

19 If you had a lump sum from a legacy to invest would you put it into:
   a. a savings account with a good interest rate?
   b. gold?
   c. gemstones?

20 Would you prefer:
   a. no pets? *b.* a dog? *c.* a cat?

The Analysis

Count how many questions you answered with a, b and c. The significant score is the letter you choose most often.

Mainly a   You have a good orderly brain. Organising, administration and logical thought come naturally to you. You could do well at science, mathematics or running a department or business. But whatever you turn your hand to you will do efficiently.

Mainly b   Your strong point is people. You are interested in them and have an instinctive understanding of them. You would shine at anything that involves caring for others – from social work and marriage guidance to running a corner shop and bringing up children.

Mainly c   You are highly creative. You have the ability to think originally but can often come up with simple solutions to problems which elude others. You could do well in one of the arts, but will also find an outlet for your talents in your hobbies and personal relationships.

52 WHAT DO YOUR CLOTHES SAY ABOUT YOU ? *(men only)*

The Test

'Clothes maketh man', they say, and what we wear says a lot about the kind of person we are. Some men are slaves to fashion, while others have worn the same suit for the last twenty years.

What do your clothes say about you?

1   If someone bought you a pink shirt would you:
     a. Consider it effeminate and not wear it?
     b. Wear it without question?
     c. Only wear it at home, not in public?

2   When do you wear a tie?
     a. Only for work
     b. Only at social functions
     c. All the time

3   Do you wear a hat?
     a. All the time   *b*. Sometimes   *c*. Never

4   Do you change into casual clothes in the evening, after work?
     a. Yes   *b*. No

5   Do you make sure that your trousers are fashionable and have turnups, or narrow legs, etc.?
     a. Yes   *b*. No

6   Do you feel good if you look smart?
     a. Yes   *b*. No, I feel uncomfortable

7   Do you wear cufflinks, tie pins or collar studs?
     a. Yes   *b*. No

8   Do you roll up your sleeves underneath a jacket?
     a. Yes   *b*. No

9   Do you like people to notice and remark on your clothes?
     a. Yes   *b*. No

10 Do you ever grasp your lapels or place your thumbs under your belt?
    a. Yes *b.* No

11 Do you change your underclothes:
    a. Daily? *b.* Alternate days? *c.* Less frequently?

12 Given the choice at a dinner party, would you wear evening dress or something less formal?
    a. Dress suit *b.* More casual wear

The Analysis

1. b If you wear it without question you have a sensible attitude to clothes. You wear something because you like it and are comfortable and do not worry what other people might think.

2. a or b You wear a tie because you think it looks smart, and when you feel it is appropriate. A tie should not be worn merely for the sake of it, and to wear a tie on any occasion is old-fashioned.

3. b Wearing a hat sometimes shows that you are a practical person, probably when weather conditions, or occasions, call for it.

4. a You have your own individual style, preferring to wear clothes that suit your personality and situation.

5. a Nothing looks worse than baggy trousers when a narrow leg is the fashion, or turnups that are long out of date.

6. a You enjoy clothes and like to look and feel smart - you like to make the effort and to be judged by your clothes.

7. *a*   These little adornments show a little extra pride and care has been taken with your appearance.

8. *b*   Rolling up sleeves shows a rebellion to dressing up and a desire for a casual look.

9. *a*   Yes, you like to make the effort and appreciate it when people notice.

10. *b*   Grasping lapels or putting your thumbs under your belt shows that you are aggressive and want to dominate. You're a much nicer person if you don't.

11. *a*   Changing daily or twice daily shows that you have a natural concern for personal hygiene.

12. *a*   If you like to dress up for a dinner party it shows that you have a sense of occasion, and feel it is a compliment to your host to make an effort with your appearance.

Give yourself 10 points for each answer that agrees with the above.

100-120   You like clothes and enjoy wearing them. You like to be fashionable and know what suits you. You may occasionally wear something that doesn't suit you - but what does that matter, so long as you have style?

60 - 90   You like to look nice, but want to be comfortable, and if it is a choice between looking sloppy and comfortable, you will look sloppy.

20-50   You are no slave to fashion and tend to be conventional in your attire. You know what suits you and stick to it, and are very unadventurous. You could perhaps smarten up a little.

10 or less   You roll your sleeves up, you don't like ties, you don't like dressing-up and wouldn't be seen dead in pink. In fact – you are an out and out slob.

53   WHAT DO YOUR CLOTHES SAY ABOUT YOU ? *(women only)*

The Test

Women have always been more fashion conscious than men, causing Oscar Wilde to remark: 'Fashion is a form of ugliness so intolerable that women have to alter it every six months.' You may not consider yourself a slave to fashion, but your clothes could say something about you as a person.

1   Do you cling to old clothes that you will never wear again, but don't like to part with?
   a. Yes *b*. No

2   As a girl did you dress in the same way as your friends – even buying something identical to that of your best friend?
   a. Yes *b*. No

3   Do you like brightly coloured clothes with a lot of sparkle?
   a. Yes *b*. No

4   Do you pay great attention to matching accessories?
     a. Yes *b*. No

5   Do you often wear wigs, false eyelashes or false finger-
     nails?
     a. Yes *b*. No

8   If you feel depressed do you dress yourself up in your
     nicest clothes to make yourself feel better?
     a. Yes *b*. No

7   If you were invited to attend a function at which
     royalty would be present would you feel embarrassed
     about dressing up in full evening dress?
     a. Yes *b*. No

8   If you had, or have, poor eyesight and had to wear
     glasses all the time would you choose contact lenses for
     vanity?
     a. Yes *b*. No

9   Do you make a conscious effort to keep to a small dress
     size?
     a. Yes
     b. No, if I put on weight I just have a larger size

10   Do you prefer wearing long skirts to short ones?
     a. Yes *b*. No

11   If it became the fashion for women to wear black all
     the time, would you adopt it?
     a. Yes, because it's fashionable
     b. No, only if it suited me

12   Do you ever worry that people might think one of your
     garments looks ridiculous but they wouldn't say so?
     a. Yes *b*. No

The Analysis

1. *b*   No, to hang on to old garments shows that you are clinging to the past out of sentiment, and are reluctant to let your youth go.

2. *b*   No, you should have dressed in your own individual style to allow your own personality to develop.

3. *b*   If you answered 'no' you have a sense of dignity and prefer style to garish colours.

4. *b*   Just as much care should be taken with accessories as with your main wardrobe.

5. *b*   No, to wear a number of false beauty aids suggests that you are dissatisfied with your own appearance and need reassurance.

6. *a*   If clothes make you feel happy you have a sensible attitude to what you wear.

7. *a*   Yes, you should dress yourself up to the nines and enjoy it. If you are embarrassed, you have little confidence in yourself.

8. *a*   Men do make passes at girls who wear glasses, and glasses can be very fetching, but if you are prepared to contemplate contact lenses, you clearly consider appearance most important.

9. *a*   Yes, you should try and retain your figure – to allow yourself to wear a larger size dress shows a lack of self-pride.

10. *a or b* The occasion usually decides this one for you. Either long or short can look elegant.

11. *b* Fashions should only be adopted if they suit you. 'You should forgive fashion everything – it dies so young.'

12. *b* You should not worry about what other people might think. As long as YOU think you look good and feel comfortable, that is all that matters.

Give yourself 10 points for each answer that agrees with the above.

100 - 120 You adore clothes, you know you look good, and you have style. You try to be fashionable and are flattered when people remark on your clothes.

60 - 90 You like to look nice and as far as your budget will allow, will try and keep up with fashion. Sometimes you wear something which may not suit you, and at times you feel self-conscious and embarrassed about your clothes.

20 - 50 You do not take as much pride in your appearance as you might do. You prefer sensible and practical clothes to anything frivolous. On social occasions, you like to dress up, but at home you can sometimes look sloppy.

10 or less   Clothes are not important to you. You prefer
warmth to fashionable clothes and would prefer
thermal knickers to a black g-string. Your mind
is perhaps on more important things.

54 DO YOU HAVE SEX APPEAL ?
(men only)

The Test

A man with sex appeal need not necessarily have bulging
muscles and a bulging wallet, teeth that twinkle like stars,
or a face like a Greek god.

Many women find bald heads sexy, love a man with good
manners and kindness rather than plenty of money. So,
how do YOU rate as a sex symbol?

1   Do you wash your hair:
    a. Daily?
    b. Twice weekly?
    c. Only when you feel it needs washing?

2   Do you go on your first date with a girl (or did you
    when you dated) bearing flowers or chocolates?
    a. Yes, always
    b. Sometimes
    c. Never, in case it doesn't work out and the money is
    wasted

3   When you meet someone you really like, do you look
    into their eyes when you talk to them?
    a. Always
    b. Occasionally
    c. Feel too embarrassed and look away

4 If you are going out for a romantic evening do you take extra care with your clothes, possibly even buying a new shirt?
   a. Always
   b. Only if it is really special
   c. No, the person must accept you as you are

5 Having fallen in love and not being sure if the feeling is mutual, do you:
   a. Make the first move?
   b. Wait until your friend mentions the subject?
   c. Assume that as nothing was said, your love is not reciprocated?

6 Do you find it easy to say those three important words, 'I love you'?
   a. Easy if you really love the person and *mean* it
   b. Easily if it will satisfy the girl and keep her quiet
   c. Have never tried saying them to anyone

7 Do you think that love and sex are the same thing and you shouldn't have one without the other?
   a. Yes *b*. No

8 What is your idea of a romantic evening?
   a. A candlelit dinner for two
   b. An evening at your place in front of the TV with your arm around her and a few cans of beer
   c. A night in the back row of a cinema

9 If you had a date with someone and didn't feel too well, would you:
   a. Ring up and cancel?
   b. Go along and not let on that anything was wrong?
   c. Get the person to come and sit with you instead?

10   If your partner bought you a tie that you detested, would you:
   a. Say 'What on earth did you buy that for?'?
   b. Thank her but tactfully put it at the back of a drawer?
   c. Thank her and wear it on dates with her to show how much you appreciate the thought?

The Analysis

1.	a - 3	2.	a - 3	3.	a - 3	4.	a - 3
	b - 2		b - 2		b - 1		b - 2

5.	a - 3	6.	a - 3	7.	a - 3	8.	a - 3
	b - 2						b - 1

9.	b - 3	10.	b - 2
			c - 3

25 - 30   You are a romantic at heart and will be sexually very appealing. You can be charming and sincere and are not the kind who is only interested in physical pleasure, but enjoy the company of interesting people too.

15 - 24   You have the latent capacity to be a sex symbol, but it doesn't always surface. You lack the confidence to have a totally satisfying relationship because you are scared of being turned down. Be bolder in your approach, and a little less self-absorbed.

14 or less   Well, you're not exactly a Romeo. You like to think you can attract anyone you want, but somehow it doesn't seem to happen. This is not because you lack sex appeal – you just don't use it properly. Be more romantic.

55 DO YOU HAVE SEX APPEAL
(women only)

The Test

Sex appeal does not necessarily mean a large bust measurement and long blonde hair. You may have more to offer than you think. See how you rate.

1 Do you wear perfume?
   a. Always – even if I'm wearing nothing else
   b. Only on very special occasions
   c. Never

2 Do you think a woman is too old to fall in love after the age of 50 and that love is only for the young?
   a. Certainly not
   b. A woman ought to be happily married by then
   c. Definitely – she should know better by then

3 If you are going out on a special date do you buy a new dress?
   a. Always
   b. Sometimes
   c. Never

4 If your boyfriend was ill and couldn't meet you as arranged, would you:
   a. Suspect he was with someone else?
   b. Sympathise and offer to go and sit with him?
   c. Finish with him and go out with someone else?

5 You are planning a quiet evening in front of the TV, your hair is a mess, and you are wearing only your bathrobe. Your boyfriend rings and says he's on his way round. Do you:

a. Tell him not to come?

b. Agree to his coming, but he must accept you as you are?

c. Quickly put on something casual so as to look attractive, but naturally appealing?

6　Do you think that love and sex are the same thing and you shouldn't have one without the other?
a. Yes *b.* No

7　If your partner wanted to take you to a pub for a drink and you wanted to go to a theatre, would you:
a. Insist that you went to the theatre?
b. Give in and go to the pub?
c. Suggest that you compromise and go for a drink after the show?

8　When you care very deeply about someone do you look straight into their eyes when you talk with them?
a. Always
b. Occasionally glance into them
c. Never, in case he gets the wrong idea

9　If you fell madly in love with a man would you:
a. Tell him so immediately?
b. Wait for him to tell you he loved you first?
c. Be subtle until you are certain the feeling is mutual? and then tentatively broach the subject?

10　If your boyfriend accidentally spilt wine in your lap, would you:
a. Fly into a rage and tell him you never want to see him again?
b. Smile sweetly and give him hell when you got home?
c. Call him a 'clot' but tell him not to worry, it won't stain?

The Analysis

1. a - 3   2. a - 3   3. a - 3   4. b - 3
    b - 1   b - 2

5. b - 1   6. a - 3   7. b - 1   8. a - 3
    c - 3   c - 3   b - 1

9. a - 1   10. c - 3
    b - 1
    c - 3

24 - 30 You are clearly a very appealing person to a man and have a great inner beauty and strength as well as being physically attractive. You take a pride in your appearance and like men who appreciate it. You like a man who is intelligent as well as good looking, and like being accepted as a person rather than a sex symbol.

15 - 23 You like to be noticed and have your own way. You are attractive, but you like to make sure it is appreciated. You are not prepared to make the effort for just any man, only for that special person, and you have no time for a man if he wounds your pride.

Less than 14 You do not make the most of your feminine charms, and are not prepared to go out of your way to attract a man, your idea being that people must accept you for what you are. Your aim in life is to find a steady, reliable person to settle down with.

56   ARE YOU A GOOD LOVER ?

The Test

No two people are alike and what is sexually stimulating to some people would turn others off. However, do you rate yourself as a good lover? Do you know that your partner is sexually fulfilled too? Or could your sex life be vastly improved with a little more imagination? Answer the following questions honestly.

1   The man should always make the first move in any relationship?
a. Yes *b.* No

2   Love is absolutely impossible without sex? Is this true?
a. Yes *b.* No

3   In a physical relationship with your partner do you find certain parts of his/her body objectionable?
a. Yes *b.* No

4   Do you feel that sex should only take place in the privacy of the bedroom?
a. Yes *b.* No

5   If your partner suggested something new in sex, would you be prepared to give it a try?
a. Yes *b.* No

6   Do you feel let down if mutual orgasm isn't achieved?
a. Yes *b.* No

7   If your partner kissed you in a public place, such as a restaurant or cinema, would you feel embarrassed?
a. Yes *b.* No

8 It has been said that every man's ideal is to find a virgin who is a whore. Do you think it is important that both partners are sexually experienced for a successful relationship?
   a. Yes *b*. No

9 Do you think that sex should always take place in the dark, or should there be subdued lighting?
   a. Subdued lighting *b*. Total darkness

10 Do you tell your partner what you enjoy most during sex?
   a. Yes *b*. No

11. Is it possible for a woman to take the dominant role in a physical relationship?
    a. Yes *b*. No

12 If your partner is not in the mood for sex would you just hold the person lovingly in your arms and not force them to do anything they did not want?
   a. Yes *b*. No

The Analysis

Score 1 point for each answer you agreed with.

1. NO   It is not necessary for the man to make the first move always, although many women do prefer it this way. It is quite acceptable for a woman to show a man her feelings and take the initiative, and it should not be seen as a threat to the male ego.

2. NO   A truly deep and fulfilling relationship is certainly possible without any kind of physical relationship whatsoever. Just as sex is possible without love, so love is possible without sex – although the ultimate aim of many is to have a successful physical and emotional relationship.

3. *NO*   If you object to a certain part of your partner's body then you must seriously rethink your feelings for this person.

4. *NO*   No, sex should not just take place in the bedroom. Nothing is more romantic than to make love on a deserted beach, or in front of a roaring log fire – there are a million and one places outside the bedroom.

5. *YES*   If this was your answer then you are an uninhibited and adventurous lover, who is prepared to experiment to the pleasure of your partner.

6. *NO*   Of course it is marvellous if you both achieve orgasm at the same time, but you should not feel let down or disappointed if it doesn't happen. Many people can have a rewarding and fulfilling sex life without ever reaching orgasm.

7. *NO*   If you answered YES then you've got quite a few hangups about your relationship.

8. *NO*   One of the greatest pleasures of sex is mutual discovery and experiencing new and exciting pleasures. Sex should not be automatic and routine, and nobody should ever reach the point where they feel they have learnt all there is to know about the subject.

9. *a*   This is purely a matter of taste but the most romantic of all is subdued lighting. People who prefer to make love in the dark are often embarrassed by their own body, or not at ease with their partner.

10. YES   It is important for a couple to be honest and discuss their likes and dislikes and be perfectly frank with each other. It is stimulating to any person to know that they are giving pleasure to their partner.

11. YES   Of course it is. It is immature of a man to think he must be dominant, and it is important for each partner to take on various roles.

12. YES   If you are a good lover you will be tender and aware of the needs of your partner. The last thing you should do if your partner is not in the mood for sex is to put out the light and turn away in a huff – that will do neither of you any good.

10 - 12   You are a very mature, caring and responsive lover. Fully aware of your partner's needs and have a rewarding sex life.

8 - 9   You are prepared to experiment with sex, but are not always perceptive to your partner's feelings, although you are on the way to being a good lover.

5 - 7   You have many inhibitions about your love life. You are not prepared to relax completely and are wary of experimenting. You can be a selfish lover too, concerned mainly with what is pleasurable to you.

Less than 5 You are immature with regard to sex, inhibited, and possibly afraid of disaster. There is much for you to learn, and you can begin by trying to relax more, and realise that there is more to being a good lover than a mechanical, physical act.

57   HAVE YOU GOT THE SEX FACTOR ?

The Test

It is more than sex-appeal – it is the *sex factor* – an extra something which really captivates the opposite sex. These factors show up in many ways – and are not exclusive to screen idols and models. Anyone can have them.

Have YOU? Check your sex factor with this test:

Women only

1   How often do you wear stockings rather than tights these days?
   a. Never *b.* Always *c.* On special occasions

2   He buys you frilly undies for Christmas. Do you:
   a. Take them back and change them?
   b. Wear them for a while to show willing?
   c. Put them on whenever you can to please him?

3   He likes short skirts but they're out of fashion. Do you:
   a. Tell him not to be so old fashioned?
   b. Wear them now and again, even if it's only round the house?
   c. Find an alternative, fashionable way of showing your legs?

4   The conversation gets round to different ways of making love. Do you:
    a. change the subject?
    b. join in?
    c. dismiss them airily as kinky?

5   It's the coldest winter for years, and bedtime. Do you:
    a. say 'To hell with appearances' and reach for the bedsocks?
    b. Choose a nice, attractive, sensible nightie?
    c. Leap into the cold sheets wearing only a whiff of perfume?

6   You're washing up and he starts getting passionate. Do you:
    a. respond enthusiastically?
    b. finish the washing up first?
    c. tell him there's a time and place for everything?

7   Where would you wear a gold chain? Would it be round your:
    a. neck? *b.* waist? *c.* ankle?

8   He calls to take you out for an important date but the weather is foul. Do you:
    a. Put on your most revealing outfit regardless and pile on the outside layers?
    b. Dig out all your thick winter woollies?
    c. Compromise with a smart but warm outfit?

9   You fancy the new sales rep at the office. Do you:
    a. Wait for him to make the first move?
    b. Ask if he's thought of joining the firm's social club?
    c. Hover around him chatting and fluttering your eyelashes?

10   On the whole how do other women feel about you? Do
     they:
     a. Like your company?
     b. Talk about you behind your back?
     c. Tell you their troubles?

Men only

1   What do you look at first when introduced to a girl?
    a. Her eyes? *b.* Her legs? *c.* Her breasts?

2   She's taken you home to meet her folks, but they're
    out. Do you:
    a. Suggest a tour of the place starting with her
         bedroom?
    b. Tell her you'll come back another day?
    c. Keep her company till they get back?

3   You've promised her a night to remember. Do you
    mean:
    a. A trip to the theatre?
    b. Dinner and dancing?
    c. A twosome at your place?

4   On a country walk it starts raining; she hasn't got a
    coat. Do you:
    a. Try and hitch a lift?
    b. Give her yours?
    c. Suggest sheltering in a handy barn?

5   Your friend and his girl break up and she cries on your
    shoulder? Do you:
    a. Promise to talk him round?
    b. Say she's better off without him?
    c. Suggest she goes out with you – just to make him
         jealous?

6   What does 69 suggest to you?
    a. A brand of Scotch?
    b. Sexual gymnastics?
    c. Your old grannie?

7   Your steady girlfriend is out of town. Would you:
    a. Spend the time writing her long letters?
    b. Have a few nights out with the boys?
    c. Get out your little black book?

8   The girl you're dating brings her friend along too. Do you:
    a. Try and dig up a pal to make a foursome?
    b. Take them both out and, on the quiet, get the friend's phone number?
    c. Have a big scene about it?

9   Your good-looking neighbour's husband is away on business. Do you:
    a. Call round one evening and ask if you can use her phone?
    b. Offer to take her down to the pub for a drink?
    c. Cut the lawn for her?

10 She sends you shopping for a frilly nightie. Do you:
    a. Ask the assistant to try it on for you?
    b. Grab the first one that looks about the right size?
    c. Ask a girl at the office to get it for you?

The Analysis

Women

1.	2.	3.	4.	5.
a - 0	a - 0	a - 0	a - 0	a - 0
b - 10	b - 5	b - 5	b - 10	b - 5
c - 5	c - 10	c - 10	c - 5	c - 10

6. a - 10	7. a - 5	8. a - 10	9. a - 0	10. a - 5
b - 5	b - 0	b - 0	b - 5	b - 10
c - 0	c - 10	c - 5	c - 10	c - 0

Men

1. a - 0	2. a - 10	3. a - 0	4. a - 0	5. a - 6
b - 5	b - 0	b - 5	b - 5	b - 0
c - 10	c - 5	c - 10	c - 10	c - 10

6. a - 5	7. a - 5	8. a - 5	9. a - 10	10. a - 10
b - 10	b - 0	b - 10	b - 5	b - 0
c - 0	c - 10	c - 0	c - 0	c - 5

Women:

70 Lonely nights aren't one of your problems. Certainly not the girl to take home to meet Mum – he'd lose you to Dad.

35 - 70 You like the men to make some of the running but you know when to turn it on. If it's a long term commitment you're after, you'll probably make it.

Under 35 No wonder your phone doesn't ring – you radiate about as much warmth as a 40 watt light bulb in an igloo. If you want a more exciting life, take a few tips from our questions.

Men

70 + If the opportunity doesn't present itself, you'll make one. You never miss a trick, do you?

35 - 70 You have an eye for the main chance but prefer the more subtle approach. You're no blatant Romeo, but you have your rewards

Not a very exciting life, is it? Why not read a few books on tactics, and try a new approach – life might be more fun.

58 COULD YOU SURVIVE STAYING SINGLE ?

The Test

Some of us were born to live happily ever after, all by ourselves – and some of us weren't. The problem is to find out whether we're a natural single, or if we would be better off wed.

The following test will tell you how much you depend on your partner, how you balance your home and career, and what your basic needs are.

Try it, even if you're married – answer yes or no.

1   Does spending a day or evening alone throw you into a panic?

2   When you are bored or alone, do you sleep more than usual?

3   Do you find yourself craving something to eat or drink when you are alone?

4   Do you often pick up the phone to call someone when you don't really have anything to talk about?

5   When you are alone, do you keep the radio or TV on constantly?

173

6   Are you unhappy taking a trip or going shopping unless you have someone with you?

7   Do you prefer your friends to discuss their problems with you instead of keeping them to themselves?

8   Are you shy about going to dinner or a cinema by yourself?

9   Has your weight increased by more than ten pounds in the last eighteen months?

10   Is the place you live in generally speaking to your liking?

11   Do you accept suggestions on the way you keep your home?

12   Do you sometimes spend more than your budget will allow?

13   When you sleep alone, do you go to bed looking as attractive as when your husband or lover is with you?

14   Do you sleep as well alone as when someone is with you?

15   After you have a quarrel with your husband or lover, do you worry about it?

16   Are you more content when you have someone around you all the time?

17   Do you feel a twinge of jealousy when you see a really happy couple together?

18   Do you want to have children?

19 Would you expect the person you live with to share the chores?

20 Do you allow your partner or friends to put their feet on the furniture?

21 Is your house always neat and in order?

22 Would you prefer your partner to keep his/her thoughts to himself/herself rather than have a disagreement?

23 Are you proud to introduce your friends to your partner?

24 Were, or are, your parents happily married?

25 Do you accept your friends for what they are and not try to convert them to your way of thinking?

The Analysis

If you answered 1 - 10 questions with YES

You would probably be better off single. You prefer to live in a world of your own making, without having to cope with someone else's problems. Satisfaction for you lies in the brief encounter.

If you answered 11 - 15 questions with YES

You are still not quite sure what kind of life you want to lead. It's just as easy for you to spend time happily alone as with someone else. You could get close to someone if he/she gave you plenty of time to be by yourself. With a bit of effort, though, marriage could suit you well.

175

If you answered 16 - 20 questions with YES	Having more time to yourself isn't as important to you as having someone who's the centre of your life, so you would probably be happier married. You adapt well to other people's needs, and a permanent relationship wouldn't make you feel you had lost your identity.
If you answered more than 20 questions with YES	You were made to marry. There's hardly a shared situation you can't cope with, and you have the knack of being able to keep a relationship fresh and interesting without making a more restless partner feel trapped.

59 WHAT DOES YOUR CAR SAY ABOUT YOU ?

The Test

In the world today there are over 300 million cars. In Britain it is estimated that 73% of the population own at least one car, and in many cases it has become one of the family and even an extension of the owner's personality. You don't see the business tycoon chugging along in a clapped out Morris Minor, or the aged Vicar swanning around in a TR7. If you are a car owner, this test is for you.

1 When you overtake an older model car than your own do you feel a sense of pride?
   a. Yes *b*. No

2   Have you given your car a name, such as 'Jessica' or
    'Henry'?
    a. Yes *b*. No

3   Do you enjoy driving as a hobby, or do you only drive
    as a necessity?
    a. As a hobby, for pleasure
    b. Only because I have to

4   If someone accidentally scratches your car, do you:
    a. fly into a rage and feel personally injured?
    b. not worry about it and cover it with paint when
       you get home?

5   Do you ever fantasise about driving and dream that
    you are a top racing driver, or own a vintage Rolls?
    a. Yes, often
    b. Never

6   Is the inside of your car:
    a. untidy, full of papers and anything you may need?
    b. neat, tidy and presentable?

7   Do you have rugs, cushions or pillows in your car, or
    fur seat covers?
    a. Yes *b*. No

8   If you were offered two jobs at the same time – one
    offers a good salary, the other a lower salary but a
    company car – which would you accept?
    a. Company car
    b. Higher salary

9   If someone annoys you on the road do you flash your
    lights, honk your horn, or make signs at them?
    a. Yes *b*. Never

10 If you have a passenger of the opposite sex with you, do you tend to show off your driving skills, drive faster and use all the gadgets that your car contains?
    a. Yes *b*. Never

11 If a member of your family were seriously injured in a car crash, would you seriously consider giving up driving yourself?
    a. Definitely not
    b. Would certainly think about it

12 Do you feel more at ease in a big car than in a small one?
    a. Big car *b*. Size not important

13 If you ordered a new car and they did not have your preferred colour in stock, would you have another colour or wait until the desired colour came in?
    a. Wait and get the colour I want
    b. Have any colour available

14 Do you have automatic transmission?
    a. Yes *b*. No

15 Do you have stickers, hanging ornaments, or nodding dogs in your car?
    a. Yes *b*. No

The Analysis

Give yourself ONE point for each 'a' answer.

13 - 15 You are obsessed with your car and see it as an extension of yourself. You feel at home inside it and have your familiar things around you. You have tried to make it reflect your personality. You love new gadgets from reclining seats to stereo cassette players and are not beyond showing off in it, especially if with a member of the opposite sex.

8 - 12   Your car is important to you, but not the most important thing in life. You could survive without it if you had to, but you would not like to be without the convenience of it. You keep it clean and cared for and are angry if someone else damages it. You consider a car a necessity rather than a luxury.

0 - 7   To you a car is merely a mode of transport. You do not always enjoy driving and wouldn't be upset if you didn't have to drive ever again. You don't approve of cars as status symbols, and wouldn't like to be judged on the appearance of your car.

60   HOW RESPONSIVE ARE YOU ?

The Test

The amount of satisfaction we get from life depends on what we put into it.

We derive little satisfaction and interest if we do not respond to life and its demands. Answer yes or no to the following questions.

1   Do you enjoy meeting people?

2   Do you find it easy to talk and to be friendly?

3   Are there always plenty of things you can talk about?

4   Are you sufficiently interested to remember what people say about themselves and their interests?

5   Are you good at remembering faces and names?

6   Do you usually associate the right face with the right name?

7   Do you miss people when they are not around and enquire after them?

8   Are you good at getting on with different types of people?

9   Would you be quick to help a stranger and the shy or socially awkward person?

10 Are you patient with old people and good with children?

11 Are you quick to spot any jobs that need doing and offer to help?

12 Do you seem to know instinctively when somebody wants to be friendly?

13 Do you 'warm up' in a friendly convivial atmosphere so that you are at your best in the social sense?

14 Do you go out expecting to enjoy yourself and in the frame of mind to help the fun along?

15 Are you often enthusiastic?

16 Are you an encourager of new ideas and activities?

17   Are you a patient, sympathetic, interested listener?

18   Are you good at sensing when people are tired, or not well, and want to be quiet?

19   Are you good at sensing when the atmosphere is getting strained and changing the subject?

20   Do you hate seeing people unhappy and want to do something about it?

The Analysis

For every YES answer give yourself 5 points.

70 +   You are certainly responsive and do not sit back and wait for life to come to you – you go and meet it.

60 - 70   You too are responsive, but have a certain reserve, and perhaps you are too concerned with your own affairs to bother about other people and things.

Less   You would appear to be insensitive and self-absorbed. The time may come when you would be thankful for other people's interest in *you* – but you will have to start reaching out now.

61   ARE YOU A 'JUNK FOOD' ADDICT ?

The Test

Junk food is fast becoming part of the everyday diet and could result in nutritional deficiencies, overweight, and poor health.

How often do you consume such foods?

1 sweets
   a. Frequently *b*. Sometimes *c*. Rarely *d*. Never

2 hot dogs
   a. Frequently *b*. Sometimes *c*. Rarely *d*. Never

3 hamburgers
   a. Frequently *b*. Sometimes *c*. Rarely *d*. Never

4 chips
   a. Frequently *b*. Sometimes *c*. Rarely *d*. Never

5 pizza
   a. Frequently *b*. Sometimes *c*. Rarely *d*. Never

6 pot noodles
   a. Frequently *b*. Sometimes *c*. Rarely *d*. Never

7 instant pudding
   a. Frequently *b*. Sometimes *c*. Rarely *d*. Never

8 ice cream
   a. Frequently *b*. Sometimes *c*. Rarely *d*. Never

9 biscuits
   a. Frequently *b*. Sometimes *c*. Rarely *d*. Never

10 potato crisps
   a. Frequently *b*. Sometimes *c*. Rarely *d*. Never

11 Chinese takeaway
   a. Frequently *b*. Sometimes *c*. Rarely *d*. Never

12 coca-cola
   a. Frequently *b*. Sometimes *c*. Rarely *d*. Never

13 instant mashed potato
     a. Frequently *b*. Sometimes *c*. Rarely   *d*. Never

14 ready-made meat pies
     a. Frequently *b*. Sometimes *c*. Rarely   *d*. Never

15 cocktail titbits
     a. Frequently *b*. Sometimes *c*. Rarely   *d*. Never

The Analysis

For each FREQUENTLY, give yourself 4 points;
for each SOMETIMES, give yourself 3 points;
for each RARELY, give yourself 2 points;
for each NEVER, give yourself 1 point.

50+   You are a junk food addict. You must start eating
         sensibly, or you are storing up serious health
         problems for later on.

40-49 You are a borderline junk food addict. Take stock
         of your diet and start substituting more nutritional
         foods.

30-39 You occasionally indulge in junk foods – now
         would be a good time to reverse the trend and
         eliminate the junk foods and drinks you now buy.

15-29 You are a very sensible eater. Continue as you are
         and you will avoid numerous health problems.

62   ARE YOU IN THE RIGHT JOB ?

The Test

Most people spend over forty years working, and an average of thirty-eight hours a week. Considering then that we spend at least 78,640 hours of our life at work, the choice of career is very important.

How do you know if your job is right for you? Let's find out.

1   Is the job you are in now the one you always intended to do?

2   Do you feel that you have learnt a lot from your job?

3   Do you think your days are rewarding and eventful?

4   Do you feel that you are appreciated?

5   Do you believe that your talents are put to good use?

6   Are you happy in your work and at harmony with your colleagues?

7   Are you satisfied with your income?

8   Do you wake up in the morning eager for the day ahead?

9   Are your chances of reaching the top of your profession good?

10   Do you ever lie awake at night worrying about your job?

11   Would you do another job if you had the opportunity?

12   If you were made redundant would you look for another job in the same line?

13   Do you feel exhausted at the end of the day?

14   Do you enjoy talking shop outside working hours?

15   Do you mix socially with your working colleagues?

16   Do you find yourself taking extended lunch hours?

17   Do you have days off work pleading indisposition?

18   Do you miss your job when you are on holiday?

19   Do you enjoy reading books about the subject that your career is concerned with?

20   Do you ever bring home work to do in the evenings?

The Analysis

Give yourself 5 points for each answer that agrees with the following:

1. Yes	2. Yes	3. Yes	4. Yes
5. Yes	6. Yes	7. Yes	8. Yes
9. Yes	10. No	11. No	12. Yes
13. No	14. Yes	15. Yes	16. No
17. No	18. Yes	19. Yes	20. Yes

85 - 100	You are at harmony with your job and in a career which you enjoy. You probably know your work inside out, and are extremely good at it.
55 - 80	There are many things about your job that you find uncongenial, although you basically enjoy the career. It is unlikely you would consider changing to a different trade or profession, but you may be happier moving to a different employer.
25 - 50	You are not at all happy with your position and may have considered alternative employment. You need the security of your job but would change it if something else came along.
20 or less	You are not in the right job at all. You find your work unfulfilling, and although it would be unwise to just give up the job, perhaps you should look round for something more satisfying.

63   ARE YOU A GOSSIP ?

The Test

Are you like a mouse and carry a tale wherever you go, or do you dislike gossip for the harm it can do?

Some say gossip is simply taking a healthy interest, while others are prepared to listen to gossip but not repeat it.

Remember, though, that whoever gossips to you is sure to gossip *about* you.

1   Do you enjoy listening to stories about your friends?

2   Are you inquisitive about your neighbours?

3   If you heard an amazing story about a friend of yours, would you feel a need to repeat it to somebody else?

4   Do you find most secrets too good to keep?

5   If you know *half* a story about someone, do you draw your own conclusions as to the rest of it before you tell it to someone else?

6   If you see your neighbour's husband with another woman, do you suspect that they are having an affair?

7   If you did suspect your neighbour of having an affair, would you feel it your duty to tell his wife/husband what you know?

8   Do you ever begin a sentence: 'Never let it be said that I'm one for gossip, but . . .'?

9   Do you ever repeat rumours to other people?

10 Do you feel that you are a good judge of character?

11 If you heard someone telling a story that you knew was false, would you put them right?

12 Do you ever eavesdrop to discover information?

The Analysis

Give yourself 1 point for every YES answer.

10 - 12   There's no getting away from it – you are an out-and-out gossip. You love hearing about other people, often suspect the worst, and will repeat what you hear, whether it comes from a reliable source or not. I shouldn't like to live next door to you.

5 - 9   You're not exactly a scandalmonger, but you're not above enjoying a juicy bit of gossip, especially if it's about someone you know. You don't like malicious gossip, but you will listen, even if you don't repeat it.

4 - 1   You pretend not to enjoy gossip, and don't go out of your way to spread it, but you will quite happily listen to others gossiping. Then you'll return home and say: Do you know what I overheard a woman saying today . . .

0   You're not a gossip – but don't gossip about it.

64   IS YOUR CHILD A BRAT ?

The Test

One definition of a brat is a child that behaves like your own, but belongs to somebody else. Nothing is worse than an impolite and unruly child. Do other people see your child as a brat?

1   If your child plays with others is he/she:
  a. Bossy and dominant?
  b. Loud and noisy?
  c. Quiet and reserved?

2   Does your child say 'please' and 'thank you'?
    a. Never
    b. Only if you demand or prompt him
    c. Always

3   Does your child ask questions:
    a. All the time?
    b. Over and over again . . . the same one?
    c. About average for his age?

4   Is your child particularly naughty?
    a. Very   *b.* Quite often   *c.* No more than the average

5   Do you ever find it difficult to control your child?
    a. Always   *b.* Sometimes   *c.* Not usually

6   Does your child answer you back rudely?
    a. Always   *b.* Most of the time   *c.* Never

7   Does your child have temper tantrums?
    a. Frequently   *b.* Sometimes   *c.* Never

8   Does your child deliberately break toys?
    a. All the time
    b. Occasionally
    c. No, he respects toys

9   Is your child a fussy eater?
    a. Yes, very   *b.* Quite   *c.* No more than any other

10 Is your child a show-off when you have guests?
    a. Always   *b.* Sometimes   *c.* Never

11 Does your child sulk?
    a. Often   *b.* Sometimes   *c.* Never

12 Will your child play happily alone or does he demand a lot of attention?
   a. Demands attention all the time
   b. Needs a lot of attention
   c. Will play contentedly alone

The Analysis

Give yourself (or your child!) 5 points for every question which you answered with 'a' or 'b'.

50-60   Sorry but your child is a first class brat, ill-mannered and badly behaved. We don't go along with the old adage that 'children should be seen and not heard' but yours can be heard even when not seen. If your child is not to grow up obnoxious he must be disciplined more now – don't allow him to dominate your life so much.

30-45   You have an unruly child who knows how to handle you and get his own way. Don't be so anxious to mop up those tears – they're often for your benefit. Show that you have the upper hand.

5-25   Your child is pretty average, no more noisy or unruly than most children, and on the whole quite well-behaved. A likeable child with a personality of his/her own. But, admit it, there are times when you are glad to get your child tucked up in bed.

0   You must have a perfect angel and should be very thankful – you must be a first class parent.

65 WHAT KIND OF CHARACTER DO YOU HAVE ?

The Test

Below is a list of adjectives that may, or may not, apply to you. Put a circle round the ten words that you can apply to yourself

1	Generous	19	Tactful
2	Bighead	20	Indecisive
3	Kind	21	Artistic
4	Selfish	22	Stubborn
5	Thoughtful	23	Emotional
6	Domineering	24	Deceitful
7	Helpful	25	Dependable
8	Untidy	26	Frigid
9	Caring	27	Warm
10	Critical	28	Boastful
11	Serious	29	Honest
12	Lazy	30	Outspoken
13	Humorous	31	Careful
14	Bad tempered	32	Tough
15	Loving	33	Self-controlled
16	Aggressive	34	Greedy
17	Adaptable	35	Practical
18	Suspicious		

The Analysis

If your ten words include six odd-numbered and four even-numbered selections then you can count yourself as a very normal person, frank and open and nice to know.

If you chose all odd-numbered words then you are a perfect angel and too good to be true (unless you cheated or are not honest about your character). If you chose all even-

191

numbered words then you are a tough, aggressive and very dominant personality, not too nice to know, and can be difficult to live with at times.

If you chose half and half then you are a well-balanced person, and your good points will outweigh your bad ones.

66   ARE YOU A TYPICAL ARIES ?

The Test

If you were born between March 21 and April 20 your star sign is Aries the Ram, one of the most egocentric signs of the Zodiac.

You may or may not believe in astrology, but see how typical you are by answering the following statements – true or false.

1   You are a leader and a fighter, determined to get your own way at all costs.

2   You sometimes get over-enthusiastic and carried away with a new plan or venture.

3   You work far better on your own than with others, preferring to be in control.

4   In your relationships as well as your career the pursuit of your ideal is much more enjoyable than the attainment.

5   You hate injustice and are prepared to fight for what you think is right.

6   You have a streak of cruelty in you and can have a very nasty temper.

7   However much your pride is hurt you can pick yourself up and start all over again.

8   You fall in love impulsively, but have high ideals and it rarely lasts long.

9   Red is your dominant colour and you feel at ease if you wear any variations of this colour. You probably have a red car too.

10 There are times when you can be unnecessarily demanding and selfish, often causing pain to others.

11 You get bored very easily and do not enjoy the mundane things in life, such as cooking and housework.

12 True Arians are of medium height and over, with long necks and high cheek bones and suffer from diseases of the head, such as dental trouble, and neuralgia.

13 You appreciate freedom more than anything and hate restrictive relationships.

14 You are a city person and hate large open spaces and the countryside.

15 You dislike compromise and want the real thing or nothing at all.

The Analysis

Count 1 point for each TRUE answer.

11 - 15   You are a typical Arian in nearly all character-
           istics.

Less   You are not typical and are dominated by your
           rising sign which has influenced your personality.

67   ARE YOU A TYPICAL TAUREAN ?

The Test

If you were born between April 21 and May 20 you were
born under the sign of Taurus the Bull, a bisexual sign of
the Zodiac that combines the masculine image of the bull
and the feminine archetype of Venus, the goddess of love.

Answer *true* or *false* to the following statements to see if
you are typical.

1   Like a bull you are patient but stubborn, refusing to
    take advice even if you believe it is the right thing to do.

2   You are slow to forget and forgive any wrongs that
    have been done to you, and are apt to brood.

3   You enjoy money and possessions and long for
    material security and comfort.

4   You are very possessive, not only about the things you
    have, but about the people you know.

5   You are a sensuous, loving person, your main desire
    being to have a secure, comfortable and stable
    relationship.

194

6   You have the power to see things through to the end, so that if you set yourself a goal your determination enables you to reach your target.

7   Although very possessive, you are unselfish and devoted to the one person you love and are unswerving in your loyalty.

8   You have a logical mind and are good in a crisis, and have the ability to stay calm.

9   You prefer anything erotic to something pornographic, preferring comfortable cosy sex on a heap of cushions rather than wild abandon on a tropical island.

10 Although practical you have artistic and creative ability, and appreciate beauty in all things.

11 You are hopeless with money and spend it too freely, regretting it when it is too late.

12 You are a well balanced and sincere person with a sense of humour, qualities you admire in other people.

13 Blue is the typical Taurean's favourite colour and any shade of this is harmonious to you.

14 The typical Taurean is squarely built with a thick neck, full forehead, lips and nostrils. They are particularly susceptible to throat disorders.

15 You give the outward appearance of strength, but deep down you are a sentimental softy at heart.

If you answered TRUE to 11 or more statements, then you are a typical Taurean.

68   ARE YOU A TYPICAL GEMINI ?

The Test

If you were born between May 21 and June 20 you were born under the sign of Gemini the Twins, the planet of communication, which means you are often more mentally aware of your surroundings than any other sign. To discover if you are a typical Gemini, answer *true* or *false* to the following:

1   You have some contradictions in your personality, hating to tell deliberate lies, but not worried about deceiving. Strong in big matters, but weak in small ones.

2   You are a great conversationalist and delight in long discussions and lengthy telephone calls.

3   You have, or will, change your career many times, probably ending up in a totally different profession to the one you started out in.

4   You are restless and motivated by curiosity, which leads you into a wide range of activities, often very different and disconnected, in search of information.

5   When the Gemini falls in love it is for keeps and will remain devoted and true until the end. You are stimulated mentally rather than physically by pornography. Once again this is your search for new information and adventure.

6   Your talents are often superficial although you try to avoid giving this impression by a flow of witty speech and a wealth of knowledge; this leads people to think that you do not take life seriously.

7   Travel is stimulating to you and you hate the thought of settling down.

8   You find fantasy more exciting than reality in your sex life, and are only really satisfied by an intelligent and expressive lover.

9   All pale colours appeal to you, such as silvery blue, green, mauve or white, and you will be at your best wearing light clothes.

10 Typical Gemini people are physically tall, with long limbs, hazel eyes and dark hair, and can suffer from lung troubles.

11 You like to look your best and keep up with the latest fashions where you can.

12 You enjoy good food and a heavy meal or plain home cooking will not appeal to you; instead you prefer delicate tit-bits, light wines and cocktail parties.

13 You have the ability to do several things at the same time, and will even have several books on the go at once.

14 'Imagination' is your key word, whatever field of activity you are participating in. You will try anything once.

15 You enjoy a weekend in the country, but anything longer than a fortnight would bore you as you crave variety.

If you answered TRUE to 11 or more statements, then you are a typical Gemini.

69   ARE YOU A TYPICAL CANCERIAN ?

The Test

If you were born between June 21 and July 20 you were born under the star sign of Cancer the Crab, which produces the most sensitive and emotional people in the Zodiac.

To see if you are typical, answer the following with *true* or *false*.

1   You have great regard for things that have happened in the past and looking back makes you feel emotionally secure.

2   There are contradictions in your character that make you appreciate your own home, but you also have a desire to wander. You are gregarious, yet happy to be alone.

3   You can be over-sensitive and take offence where none is intended.

4   You usually take the line of least resistance and are easily persuaded by other people, yet once your mind is made up, nothing will sway you.

5   You are intuitive and a good judge of character, knowing the kind of people that appeal to you.

6   You are good in a crisis and are the one who arrives with the brandy and beef broth in an emergency.

7   Romance is important to you and you crave affection, but unfortunately this craving can cause you to smother your loved one.

8   In any physical relationship you like to be dominant, but will not make the first move unless your partner gives a sign of assent.

9   Animals are important to you and you have more than one pet. You abhor cruelty to animals.

10 You prefer living in the country or beside the sea, feeling stifled in a large city. Periods of solitude in open spaces help you to relax and rejuvenate your spirit.

11 Your partner must have strength and support you, wiping your tears if necessary. You bottle up your emotions and disappointments and it is only with a strong and reassuring person that you can release the tension.

12 Although green is often considered to be unlucky, the Cancer person feels at ease in this colour and will allow it to dominate his or her surroundings. Again, the greens of the countryside are appreciated.

13 The true Cancer type is of medium height, inclined to stoutness, short nose, pale complexion, grey or light blue eyes, and prone to gastric troubles.

14 You appreciate an exciting career, the sparkle and bright lights of showbusiness, but at the same time need your own quiet little nest to return to at the end of the day.

15 You love beauty and harmony, and art galleries and museums appeal to you.

If more than 11 statements were TRUE about you then you can say you are a typical Cancerian.

The Test

If you were born between July 21 and August 20 you are one of the 'sunshine people' born under the sign of Leo the Lion, a vibrant person who attracts others.

To discover if you are the true Leo type, answer the following statements about yourself with *true* or *false*.

1   Your lifestyle speaks for you. You have a tendency to be flamboyant, and like to have recognition to pander to your ego.

2   You are a strong character, knowing exactly what you want from life and are determined to get it.

3   You have great common sense, and are usually optimistic in your outlook; you also have an abundance of vitality.

4   You have a sense of dignity that commands respect and you are very loyal; if you are not careful, however, this dignity can lead to arrogance and conceit.

5   You love money and the things it will buy, and can be too extravagant.

6   You are creative, as long as your talents are seen. You would need to be the actor, not the backstage hand, wanting the limelight.

7   You love crowds, parties, theatres, and anywhere that people congregate.

8   You love clothes, but can overdress at times, and wear colours that are much too bright.

9   You are not favourable towards marriage. When you love you are prepared to give your all, but demand complete devotion in return, which could be your downfall.

10   Your impulsive nature will lead you to fall in love more than once, and it is not beyond you to contemplate a discreet affair, causing you to be unfaithful to your lover, even though you deeply regret it afterwards.

11   Orange and gold are important colours and will dominate your home and wardrobe.

12   *Noblesse Oblige* is your motto, and although you may often feel hurt you heal very quickly and soon bounce back.

13   Leo people are often tall with large bones, upright in posture, with a florid complexion. They are liable to heart disorders.

14   In any physical relationship the Leo is timid of making the first move for fear of rejection, but needs only a little encouragement – a nod or a wink.

15   You enjoy eating in restaurants where the waiters hasten to satisfy your every need. This is far more satisfying than a quick hamburger or a Chinese takeaway.

If you answered more than 11 statements with TRUE you are a typical Leo.

71   ARE YOU A TYPICAL VIRGO ?

The Test

If you were born between August 21 and September 20 you fall under the star sign of Virgo the Virgin, one of the three Earth signs, and possessing very high personal standards.

To see if you live up to Virgo's reputation, answer the following statements with *true* or *false*.

1   You enjoy life in the country, having been born at a beautiful time between Summer and Autumn, and a garden is a must to you.

2   You are quiet and reserved, with good mental qualities, but success has never been easy and you have only got anywhere by really putting your mind to the necessary work.

3   You desire perfection in all things, which can cause relationship problems when trying to find a partner who lives up to your standards.

4   You are almost obsessive about cleanliness and personal hygiene, and at times much too house-proud.

5   Your enjoyment of a sexual relationship can often be ruined by your analytical nature and clinical approach to life. You would rather be forewarned so that you know exactly where you are.

6   You are careful with your money, buying sensible and practical clothes rather than anything wild or extravagant.

7   You value worldly possessions and having your own house and land is important to you. Not because you are a snob, but because it satisfies your need to have your possessions close to you.

8   Your health matters, and you adopt special diets and food fads, and exercise when possible.

9   You are not a party-loving person, and would rather entertain individual friends one at a time than throw a party for them all.

10 You are intolerant of fools and stupidity.

11 You do not find it easy to show your feelings, but you are affectionate. Mutual respect is more important to you than physical attraction.

12 Your heart is not easily broken and if somebody lets you down, you can become absorbed in something else and take your mind off the hurt.

13 White and light shades are the colours that appeal to you and you hate bright or gaudy colours.

14 You are of medium height, neat in appearance, with blue eyes and dark hair. You are liable to digestive troubles.

If more than 11 statements are TRUE about you, you are a typical Virgo.

72 ARE YOU A TYPICAL LIBRAN ?

The Test

If you were born between September 21 and October 20 you were born under the sign of Libra the Scales, the only Zodiac sign not to be represented by a living creature.

People born under this sign generally balance between a love of justice and a need for beauty, and day and night are of equal importance to them.

To find out if you are typical, answer the following statements with *true* or *false*.

1   You are restless by nature and are fond of travel and change.

2   You appreciate luxury, whether in food, furniture or sex, and only want the best.

3   You have a strong sense of justice and an ability to see both sides of an argument.

4   In a physical relationship you need to be stimulated and prefer variety and excitement, but you need a balance between sexual gratification and intellectual fulfilment.

5   You prefer an unusual and creative career to a mundane 9 to 5 job, again because you need mental stimulation, and you have a desire to earn plenty of money to achieve the lifestyle you enjoy.

6   You hate domestic chores and would rather have a passionate Latin lover than live a steady uneventful married life.

7   Your constant need for stimulation brings conflict to relationships.

8   You have a habit of comparing everything, never being able to settle for one ideal in case you are missing out on something else. This happens in your emotional life too, making it difficult for you to choose between two people.

9   One major fault with you is day-dreaming, and difficulty in making up your mind. You would prefer someone else to make the decisions.

10   You like to keep your private and public lives separate, maintaining an even balance, and prefer social gatherings in places other than your own home.

11   When you have found your ideal partner you will put up with any kind of emotional hurt from them, remaining committed, and taking the ups and downs in your stride.

12   You love elegant restaurants and exciting foods, and adore plenty of seasoning and unusual dishes.

13   Blue, especially dark blue, is your colour. You feel discordant with light colours and will prefer dark browns, burgundies and blacks.

14   The Libra build is tall and well-made, inclining to stoutness in old age, long noses and sharp eyes. You are inclined to suffer from skin conditions and bowel disorders.

15 You have a great sense of humour, which can hide
    deceptive qualities deep within you.

If more than 11 statements were TRUE about you, you are
a well-balanced Libra.

73 ARE YOU A TYPICAL SCORPIO

The Test

If your birthday falls between October 21 and November 20
then your star sign is Scorpio the Scorpion, and you have
mystical and sensual qualities.
   To discover how true you are to your sign, answer the
following statements with *true* or *false*.

1 You are a very sensitive and emotional person, and
   your feelings are easily hurt; sometimes you feel as
   though you have been walked over with hobnail
   boots.

2 You have a sting in your tail, and although you are a
   good friend, you are a bad enemy, and pay people back
   with double the interest.

3 You are forceful and have the power to persuade
   people with your silver tongue, and you put your heart
   and soul into any cause you believe in.

4 You are very secretive and at times feel insecure,
   especially where emotional relationships are concerned.

5   You have a scientific nature and are interested in anything electrical or chemical.

6   In sexual relationships you are the dominant partner and need the other person to be submissive.

7   You lead a hectic social life, yet paradoxically you much prefer to be alone because you feel strangely separate and like your privacy respected.

8   You like to succeed in all you set out to do, and if you should fail then you seek revenge.

9   You are a devoted partner and parent, just so long as you are allowed to rule the roost and take charge.

10 To you sex is a serious and secretive business. You find it hard to talk about, even to your partner.

11 You are attracted to water, and will feel at your happiest beside a river or the sea.

12 You are the first to admit that you are not easy to get along with, and can be very hard on yourself, blaming yourself for faults or insecurities.

13 You like many shades of colour, but hate dark colours and black in particular.

14 Scorpio people are squarely built, of medium height, with aquiline features. Particularly susceptible to nose-bleeds and bladder disorders.

15 You have a large appetite and enjoy long intimate meals with the person you love.

If more than 11 statements were TRUE about you then you are a typical Scorpio.

74   ARE YOU A TYPICAL SAGITTARIAN ?

The Test

Born between November 21 and December 20 your star sign is Sagittarius the Archer, the wanderer of the Zodiac.

To discover if you are a true Sagittarian, answer the following statements with *true* or *false*.

1   You adore travel and being able to wander from place to place, meeting new people and gaining new interests.

2   You are quick-witted and resourceful, like an archer, with plenty of energy and determination, and are reluctant to interfere in the lives and problems of others.

3   You love animals and seem to have a certain influence with them, making them attracted to you.

4   You have a tendency to be fault-finding, and at times selfish.

5   You take offence and get upset easily, often when no offence is meant.

6   Your search for a loving partnership is often hindered by your distancing yourself, and your fear of being tied down.

7   You are gregarious and enjoy the company of lots of people, yet at heart there is a lonely and wandering spirit within you. Although you need love, you must feel free.

8   You are impulsive in business affairs and will often drop one business and adopt another in a short space of time.

9   You are hungry for experience and enter into everything with enthusiasm. When you fall in love, you fall hard. You travel far, and read widely, qualities which make you attractive to others.

10 Your weakness is that it takes a lot to satisfy you and you do not always complete what you set out to do, but get sidetracked on the way.

11 You can be very outspoken and often unintentionally wounding with your blunt speech. Tact is not your strong point.

12 Physically you tend towards being clumsy and accident prone. You are the sort who has the bed collapse under you.

13 You are not always completely faithful to your partner, although a lasting relationship is your ultimate desire.

14 Purple is the colour that influences you most, and rich deep golds. You feel comfortable in all shades of purple, from lightest mauve to deepest black.

15 Sagittarians are slender, tall but inclined to stoop, have oval faces, dark eyes and good skin. Prone to rheumatic trouble and nervous disorders.

If more than 11 statements were TRUE about you, then you are a true archer at heart.

75 ARE YOU A TYPICAL CAPRICORN ?

The Test

If you were born between December 21 and January 20 you were born under the sign of Capricorn the Goat, the practical sign of the Zodiac, making you a natural executive. To see if you are typical of this sign, answer the following statements with *true* or *false*.

1 You are patient and plodding and succeed eventually through hard work. Unfortunately you never seem to have that flash of luck that alters your entire life.

2 You keep your emotions and ambitions very much to yourself, and would probably surprise a lot of people if they knew the real you.

3 You tend to look on the black side. If things did not work out in the past, you don't expect anything better next time.

4 As a lover you are faithful and passionate, but you are not prepared to settle down until you achieve your material aims and establish a secure nest first.

5   You probably take life much too seriously. There are many people with a sense of humour which you just do not understand.

6   For your personality to grow you need constant reassurance and support, respect from others and emotional security.

7   Your practical nature makes you appreciate responsibility and you are not afraid of hard work; you are a good organiser too.

8   Your major fault is that you brood about wrongs done to you and are reluctant to tell people that you are hurt. You are also very indecisive, never quite making up your mind.

9   You have a suspicious streak, often not trusting someone who is very reliable. This takes you a long time to find the perfect partner, but when you do it is for ever.

10 Your practical nature enables you to analyse situations and find a solution to problems. You may be considered conservative at times, but you are really ahead of your time because of your perceptiveness.

11 You are often your own worst enemy, not possessing enough self-respect and having a poor opinion of your abilities and achievements.

12 Not being very extrovert, you enjoy small intimate gatherings but are not at ease at big parties and social occasions.

13 Blue is the colour that dominates and you feel at ease in any shade of this colour.

14 The Capricorn type is of medium height, thin with a long nose, a narrow chin and thin neck. Eyes and hair are often dark. Liable to colds and rheumatic diseases.

15 You prefer slow and sensual lovemaking and will often end up with a partner much younger in age – but whoever it is, your partner must be responsive and receptive to your needs.

If more than 11 statements were TRUE about you then you can say you are a typical Capricorn.

76   ARE YOU A TYPICAL AQUARIAN ?

The Test

If your birthday falls between January 21 and February 20, you were born under the sign of Aquarius the Water Carrier, the most intellectual sign of the Zodiac. To discover if you are typical of your sign, answer *true* or *false* to the following statements.

1 You are greatly attracted to the arts and anything to do with drama, art or literature holds a great fascination for you.

2 Intellectual stimulation is essential to you and you tend to back away from emotional involvements because you need a clear mind, and need to feel independent.

212

3   You tend to dwell on personal grievances and are frequently dissatisfied with your surroundings.

4   You hate anything conventional and go out of your way to be non-conformist.

5   You are generally optimistic, and with most problems believe there will be some twelfth hour solution to come to your rescue.

6   Your independent spirit makes it difficult for you to work under other people and you work best when you are your own boss.

7   You are frequently unpredictable and surprise even those closest to you. This occasionally causes you to be labelled unreliable, which is not always a fair judgement.

8   You often blunder headlong into new ventures without seriously considering the consequences.

9   You have the infuriating habit of expressing your own firm opinions, will not be swayed from the stand you take, then suddenly a fresh idea enters your mind and you completely alter your position.

10   In a physical relationship you are usually the passive partner, but technique is important to you and you like to feel that what you do is the acceptable thing.

11   Although you may have financial problems they do not worry you personally unless you feel that your family will suffer, and then you worry excessively on their behalf.

12 Because you are interested in many things you lack powers of concentration and your mind flits about from one thing to another.

13 Blue is your favourite colour.

14 Aquarians are above medium height, well-built with oval faces, and light coloured eyes. Prone to nerve and blood disorders.

15 Because you have a need to be different, you accept and tolerate change, and do not worry about being the odd one out.

If more than 11 statements were TRUE about you then you are a typical Aquarian.

77 ARE YOU A TYPICAL PISCES ?

The Test

If your birthday falls between February 21 and March 20 you were born under the sign of Pisces the Fishes, symbolised by two fishes swimming in opposite directions showing the dual personality of Pisces people.

To discover how typical you are of your star sign, answer the following statements about yourself with *true* or *false*.

1 There are two sides to your nature often causing you to take a course of action which you feel is wrong. You may be asked to help an undeserving person and you do so out of pity, knowing that you are being imposed upon. You have a vivid imagination and sometimes embroider the truth to shield yourself from trouble.

2   Your dual personality pulls you between a strong desire to gratify your own ego and a feeling of insecurity and insignificance.

3   You are an incurable romantic and have an idealised view of life and relationships, closing your eyes to the unpleasant things in life whenever possible.

4   You are adaptable and can make yourself popular in almost any company, and are always sympathetic.

5   You are creative and have a powerful imagination, especially if allowed to work alone. You are blessed with an excellent memory and like to add to your general knowledge.

6   You believe wholeheartedly in your ideals and are prepared to throw yourself tirelessly into any project which would achieve them.

7   Proud and independent, your greatest fear is financial insecurity. One side of your nature leans towards a lavish lifestyle, but the other forces you to save – not always in the wisest way – often becoming 'penny wise and pound foolish'.

8   There are times when you feel down, full of self-pity and unwilling to accept the responsibility for things you have done, but this doesn't last long.

9   Love and sex are important to you and you need someone who will reciprocate your love. You would become completely dependent upon such a person.

10 Emotional and financial stability are essential to your well-being, but your partner must have great understanding, and be supportive.

11 When you are in love you give of yourself completely, indeed can be almost overpowering. You seek to please your partner, praise the good points and forget the bad.

12 Pisceans have immense potential in their careers, they trust their intuition, use their imagination, and make use of every possible opening. Everything has to pander to their ego in the process, otherwise they are not interested. Pisceans are one of the most egocentric groups in the Zodiac.

13 The Pisces type are of medium build, have sloping shoulders and often inclined to stoop. They have full, light coloured eyes, short limbs, plentiful dark hair, and clear skins. Particularly susceptible to tumours and infectious diseases.

14 Blues and any shade of mauve are colours which influence you most.

15 The perfect way to seduce a Piscean is over a long, lingering candlelit meal, plenty of wine and, of course, seafood.

If 11 or more statements were TRUE about you, then you are a typical Pisces.